COVER: Pietro Dandini, *Allegory of Painting*, No. 14, Private Collection

FRONSTIPIECE: Cristofano Allori, *Judith with the Head of Holofernes No. 1,* lent with the gracious permission of H.M. The Queen

Painting in Florence

1600-1700

Foreword by Sir Harold Acton, C.B.E.
Catalogue by Charles McCorquodale

Royal Academy of Arts
20th January - 18th February 1979

Fitzwilliam Museum, Cambridge
27th February - 28th March 1979

A Royal Academy Exhibition presented by
COLNAGHI

Catalogue sponsored by FIAT (U.K.) Ltd.

SPONSORS

FIAT (U.K.) LTD.

Riunione Adriatica Sicurtà,
the International Insurance Group,
and its UK subsidiary,
British Reserve Insurance Company Ltd.

COLNAGHI is pleased to announce that The Department of Tourism of the Regional Government of Tuscany, in co-operation with the Italian State Tourist Office, will offer a holiday prize of one week for two people in a first-class hotel in Florence, during 1979 (excluding April, September and October), flying Alitalia. This prize will be found in one of the catalogues on sale at the Royal Academy.

ACKNOWLEDGMENTS

We are most grateful firstly to the lenders, who are listed on the following page, and to our sponsors for their enlightened patronage, without which this exhibition would not have been possible on this scale. In the first place, Fiat (UK) Ltd. have underwritten the cost of the catalogue and the poster, and it is this particularly generous gesture that has made it possible to offer the catalogue at a very attractive price. The Riunione Adriatica di Sicurtà, through its subsidiary, the British Reserve Insurance Company, has also made a very generous contribution to the costs, and this has made certain other aspects of this exhibition much more satisfactory. The Arts Council has made a grant to the Fitzwilliam Museum to enable the exhibition to be shown in Cambridge, and has also helped the organisers with the transport of some of the paintings.

We are also especially grateful for the collaboration of the President of the Royal Academy ,Sir Hugh Casson, who has taken an active interest in the show from the outset. And it is a great pleasure to be able to include as a Foreword the introduction to Florentine painting written by Sir Harold Acton. The exhibition itself was the brain-child of Mr. Charles McCorquodale, and he has worked on it with unflagging effort. The catalogue he has produced is a notable contribution to scholarship in the field, in which he is an acknowledged expert. We have also enjoyed working with the staff of the Royal Academy, notably the Secretary, Mr. Sidney Hutchison, Mr. Norman Rosenthal, and Miss Griselda Hamilton-Baillie.

We also thank His Excellency Dr. Roberto Ducci, the Italian Ambassador, for his interest and encouragement; also Consigliere Guido Lenzi ,and Professor Mario Montuori, Director of the Italian Institute. Signor Giampiero Gallian, Director of the Italian State Tourist Office in London, put us in touch with the Regional Government of Tuscany, and both have brought an awareness of this artistic event to a wider public.

We are much indebted to Sir Oliver Millar, Surveyor of The Queen's Pictures, Mr. Michael Levey, Director of the National Gallery, and Mr. James White, Director of the National Gallery of Ireland, and Professor Michael Jaffé, Director of the Fitzwilliam Museum. We would also like to acknowledge the unstinting support of Mr. Jack Baer, Mr. Hugh Brigstocke, Miss Joanna Drew, Mr. Dennis Farr, Mr. Leslie Harris, Mr. Homan Potterton, Sir Ellis Waterhouse, Mr. Michael Wynne and many others. And finally, but not least, the hardworking patience of Mrs. Pamela Grundy at Colnaghi's.

CLOVIS WHITFIELD

P. & D. Colnaghi & Co. Ltd., 14 Old Bond St., London, W.1.

LENDERS

Her Majesty The Queen
Ashmolean Museum, Oxford
City of Birmingham Museums and Art Gallery
Viscount Coke
P. & D. Colnaghi and Co. Ltd.
Sir Francis Dashwood, Bt.
The Marquess of Exeter, K.C.M.G.
Fitzwilliam Museum, Cambridge
Brinsley Ford, Esq.
Glasgow Museum and Art Galleries
Guildhall Art Gallery
Lorth Methuen, A.R.I.C.S.
National Gallery of Ireland, Dublin
Trustees of the National Gallery, London
Trustees of the Duke of Newcastle
City Museum and Art Gallery, Plymouth
Viscount Scarsdale
Trustees of the Bowood Settlement
Southampton Art Gallery
Ulster Museum
and those who wish to remain anonymous

FOREWORD

In his provocative lecture on 'Art History as an Academic Study' delivered at Cambridge in 1933 Roger Fry remarked that the Seicento had become once more the subject of serious study and 'even a second-rate artist like Magnasco has a society devoted to his cult'. In fact Magnasco's name was chosen as a brilliant protagonist of Seicento *coloratura* in painting, as a master of 'the rapid, nervous brush-stroke and of magic light effects', to quote Rudolf Wittkower. Though he spent a fruitful decade in Florence he was Genoese, and therefore is not included in this Florentine exhibition. Considering the Bloomsbury cocoamongers sponsored by Fry at the Omega workshops his dismissal of Magnasco as second-rate is absurd, and the society, which was not devoted to his cult, was refreshingly eclectic. Carlo Dolci's fine portrait of Sir Thomas Baines, here on loan from the Fitzwilliam Museum, Cambridge, was among its sensational exhibits some forty years ago.

Thanks to a galaxy of art historians, since 1933 there has been 'a reversal of generally accepted aesthetic judgements' in favour of seventeenth-century Italian painting and this exhibition, organised by Messrs P. & D. Colnaghi in collaboration with Mr. Charles McCorquodale, should open our eyes to the peculiar excellence of many Florentine artists whose work has not been published or exhibited previously. It constitutes a microcosm of the Florentine Seicento whose art has too often been ignored, though many of its masterpieces were brought to light in 'The Twilight of the Medici' exhibition held at the Detroit Institute of Arts and the Palazzo Pitti in 1974, followed by an ingenious reconstruction of Don Lorenzo de' Medici's picture gallery held at the villa of Poggio a Caiano in 1977.

Faithful to family tradition the later Medici, from the Grand Duke Cosimo II who succeeded his father in 1609, to the Grand Prince Ferdinando who died in 1713, were discriminating patrons of the fine arts. If the glory had departed, its afterglow lingered with golden gleams throughout the century. Galileo's discoveries and inventions, and those of his disciples, stimulated experiments with new forms of expression in the visual arts. The revolt against conventional Cinquecento Mannerism was led by Lodovico Cigoli, a friend and correspondent of Galileo, who approved of his theory that beauty is the product of a strict adherence to truth of observation, of a geometric arrangement of shapes and spaces, and of the elimination of unnatural distortion.

Cosimo II was a pupil and protector of Galileo, who christened Jupiter's satellites *Sidera Medicea* in his honour. Unfortunately Cosimo was an invalid from the age of twenty-four until he died in 1620 at the age of thirty. From his mother Christine of Lorraine he inherited a taste for northern painting, which accounts for the numerous genre pictures and landscapes on copper and stone he collected. Jacques Callot came to Florence from Lorraine at this period, whose pageants and festivals and scenes of popular life he etched with supreme elegance and gusto.

Justus Sustermans, a native of Antwerp, made so strong an impression on Cosimo that he was appointed court painter with a good salary and lodgings in the palace: for the next sixty years, until he died in 1681, he portrayed three generations of the later Medici male and female, jaunty cardinals and gloomy princesses, scholars, priests, nobles and commoners. His portraits bestride the Seicento and print his models on our memory. 'A master of the official international style of portraiture which developed in the wake of Van Dyck,' as Wittkower described him, he was a friend of Rubens as well as of Van Dyck, who etched his likeness in ebullient youth. Here, we have a splendid example of his female portraiture, and, from the Ashmolean Museum, Oxford, a preliminary study for the largest and least typical of his early Florentine compositions which, like so many first impressions is more pleasing than the finished product. It is an eloquent record of court ceremonial: the Florentine senators—how dignified in their black robes—swearing allegiance to young Ferdinando II after his father Cosimo's death. Seated between his mother, the Austrian Archduchess Maria Maddalena who commissioned the painting, and his grandmother Christine of Lorraine on a dais heavily draped in black, the pale boy receives homage from the chief magistrate Bartolommeo Concini, brother of the notorious Maréchal d'Ancre, kneeling at the foot of the throne, while the other senators are skilfully grouped around him, austere individuals with fashionable goatees. In the foreground on the left a muscular old man reclines naked beside a jar of water symbolizing the river Arno; behind him stands a female figure of Tuscany in a gown trimmed with ermine, flourishing a crown towards the juvenile sovereign. Thus allegory is gracefully combined with realism. Later on Sustermans was to portray Ferdinando II in a variety of attitudes and costumes. As I have written elsewhere, the effect of gallant majesty is achieved in many ways—by the aid of swirling satin cloaks trimmed with hot miniver and delicate frozen lace; or the tremendous flopping hat of a cavalier bedecked with ostrich plumes; or of flashing decorative armour. Without flattering his models he gave them a certain grandeur and nobility. His portrait of Galileo was worthy of Rubens, and it is scarcely surprising that the silvery tones and patina of his other canvases reminded Burckhardt of Velazquez.

Though Cosimo II died so young his court was a republic of art and science, and perhaps because his health was so wretched he was attracted to painters who could amuse and entertain him. The delicate touch, translucent colours, and above all the typically Tuscan humour of Giovanni da San Giovanni, whose *Pievano Arlotto playing a practical joke on some huntsmen* is shown here, appealed to him more than other contemporary Florentines.

Giovanni da San Giovanni's brief picaresque existence as chronicled by Filippo Baldinucci—he died aged forty-four—reflects the brighter side of the Seicento, transforming myths, legends and allegories into episodes of actual life, free from the academic conventions of his distinguished master Matteo Rosselli, whose *Triumph of David* is at Kedleston. Even his paintings of religious subjects reveal more humour than piety. He chose his models among friends and foes, depicting the latter in some repulsive role, as an executioner in *The Beheading of St John the Baptist*, or as a devil stoned by young angels, or as a lecherous satyr. A *pleinairiste* rather than a studio painter, spontaneous and impressionistic, he surpassed himself in frescoes of which even G. B. Tiepolo would not have been ashamed. Those in the Sala degli Argenti of the Pitti palace are painted in his happiest vein of bucolic lyricism, a vein similar to Pontormo's lunettes in Poggio a Caiano, beside which the other frescoes by Cecco Bravo, Vannini and Furini in the same hall seem pompous and prosaic. He was a martyr to gout at the time (1635) which probably caused his angry dismissal of Il Volterrano, his assistant. The frescoes were interrupted by his death in 1636. He is an eccentric for whom we feel a personal affection.

Giovanni kept aloof from his jealous colleagues and founded no school. Il Volterrano, who collaborated with him briefly in the Pitti, came closest to his style before succumbing to the influence of the Romanized Tuscan Pietro da Cortona in later years. He, too, left a famous picture of the *Burla del pievano Arlotto*, (now in the Pitti), which appealed so much to Cosimo II that he had two versions made. In one of these the wily parish priest, a legendary practical joker, arrives at an inn soaking wet, and seeing that the only fire is monopolized by peasants he pretends to have lost his money on the road owing to a hole in his purse. The peasants creep out into the darkness to look for the coins— and the priest has the fire to himself.

Dinners were often occasions for practical jokes which seem to have enjoyed a general appeal. After his quarrel with Giovanni da San Giovanni Il Volterrano was engaged by Don Lorenzo de' Medici, Cosimo II's younger brother, to decorate the loggia of his Villa Petraia, where he worked from 1636 to 1646 with intervals for study in Venice and Parma under the aegis of his generous patron. After Don Lorenzo's demise in 1649, Il Volterrano was captivated by the dynamism of Pietro da Cortona, (who frescoed four ceilings in the Pitti palace between 1640 and 1647), and he experienced a complete change of style. The paintings of *Diana resting* and *Hylas* exhibited here are in his exhilarating early manner, vying with the best of Giovanni da San Giovanni. What a difference between the styles of these masters and that of Carlo Dolci, yet each represents a characteristic phase of the Tuscan Seicento. Giovanni da San Giovanni and Il Volterrano were immune from the blast of the Counter-Reformation, which might have predominated during the long reign of Grand Duke Cosimo III, had not his elder son, the Grand Prince Ferdinando, a fastidious connoisseur, been anxious to infuse fresh life into a stagnant school.

Owing to the tribe of his mediocre imitators it is easy to lose sight of the originality of Carlo Dolci, who is amply represented here. A genuine technical prodigy who painted his masterly portrait of Ainolfo de' Bardi at the age of sixteen, he became a byword for his morbid piety, having vowed his talent to religious images. As an inspired medium of the Counter-Reformation he was cherished by the bigoted Cosimo III and his even more bigoted mother, Vittoria della Rovere, who led the fashion for his cabinet pictures of ecstatic saints. His biography by Baldinucci would be laughable were it not so pathetic. We may marvel at his 'enamelled brilliance of colour' and 'exquisite finish', yet we are thankful that, as Mr McCorquodale has observed in a sympathetic essay, he stands outside the main stream of Florentine Seicento painting. His languishing Virgins are the very quintessence of *bondieuserie*, yet he could paint the adipose dowager Grand Duchess, who doted on him, with cruel exactitude. His superb portrait of Sir Thomas Baines suggests what he might have become without his religious mania. Always painstakingly deliberate—he would spend a whole week perfecting a hand or foot—he was deeply humiliated by the Neapolitan Luca Giordano when he came to Florence boasting of his rapidity and mocking Carlino's slowness. Baldinucci attributes his mortal depression to an increasingly acute sense of his own inferiority, though his paintings were greatly in vogue with the wealthy nobility. His 'Madonna and Child' in a sumptuous frame of jasper, gilt-bronze ornaments and fruit carved in *pietre dure* (Florence, Pitti) was designed for the ill-starred wedding of Prince Gian Gastone. His *Flight into Egypt* visible here, was one of the nine paintings commissioned from him by the 5th Lord Exeter, who also ordered fifteen from Luca Giordano, as Professor Haskell informs us in his scholarly *Patrons and Painters* (1963). It is comforting to know that these extremes still meet in the Exeter Collection.

Most of the painters represented in this exhibition belong to the golden age, the first half of the seventeenth century, when Cigoli and Matteo Rosselli were the leading masters. Both Cristofano Allori, who according to Lanzi was considered the greatest painter of this epoch 'though vicious habits often seduced him from his labours'; the Fleming Giovanni Biliverti, whose *Miracle of St. Zenobius* is one of his most vividly Florentine performances; and Jacopo da Empoli, a magnificent draughtsman, is still unduly neglected; were followers of Cigoli. Among Empoli's pupils Felice Ficherelli, so silent and phlegmatic that he was nicknamed *Felice Riposo*; Giovanni Martinelli; Francesco Furini, also a pupil of Rosselli; were the most eminent.

Baldinucci reproached Furini for depicting so many female nudities 'thus endangering good morals', but it is for the sensuous flesh tones of his women that he is admired, a precursor of our Etty. He spent lavishly on his models yet was ordained a priest in his fortieth year. His *Hylas and the Nymphs* —the former in contemporary costume with a plumed cap standing on the shore while the sea nymphs swim towards him and compete for his seduction—is an undoubted masterpiece with more than a hint of Guido Reni. Lorenzo Lippi was another disciple of Rosselli whose naturalistic portraits were superior to such ingenious compositions as his *San Saverio recovering from the claws of a crab the Crucifix which he had dropped into the sea*. He is equally famous among philologists for his mock-heroic poem *Malmantile Racquistato* 'sprinkled with those graceful Florentine idioms that are regarded as the Attic salt of Italy', and embalming much Tuscan folklore.

After the middle of the century Pietro da Cortona ruled the roost. Some of the pleasing and prolific Dandini family, of whom Cesare was the most popular, and the exotic Fleming Livio Mehus, were his most successful pupils, though Mehus developed a highly individual style in his small easel paintings, of which the four landscapes from Holkham are notable examples.

With Giovan Camillo Sagrestani and his pupil Matteo Bonechi, who imitated his master's style to perfection, we approach eighteenth-century Rococo. Sagrestani's *Episode from the Life of St Verdiana* has the rapid, nervous brush-strokes we associate with Magnasco, and the composition reminds us of G. M. Crespi, the Grand Prince Ferdinando's favourite.

After visiting this exhibition, who could deny that the later Medici lent invaluable assistance in the protection and development of art as the leaves of a long autumn fell thick and fast on their declining dynasty?

Harold Acton

INTRODUCTION

No period in the history of painting falls into neglect without reason. In the case of 17th century Florence, the reasons are complex, and lie as much in social history and moral attitudes as in the vagaries of art-historical fashion. Carlo Dolci, described by Bürger at the Manchester Exhibition of 1857 as "...*un maître si rare, si fin, si precieux, si coquet, si chéri des ladies anglaises, et payé si cher par si gentlemen*..." and by Passavant in 1836 as "*that favourite of the English*", had sunk so low in British estimation that one of his most beautiful altarpieces was sold in London in 1957 for £90 and promptly cut into saleable but pictorially meaningless fragments. The invective poured out by Ruskin in such sour doses against Dolci and all he stood for turned the tide of taste against the whole Florentine Seicento, and closed the eyes of subsequent generations to one of the most colourful schools in Italian painting. Coincidentally with the revaluation of Baroque art in the wake of the German art historian Heinrich Wölfflin's *Kunstgeschichtliche Grundbegriffe* of 1915 (translated as *Principles of Art History* in 1932), the foundation of the Bauhaus cast a threatening shadow over any art which might be termed 'decadent'. All those dusty corners of art in which the great nostalgics of the early part of this century such as Ronald Firbank liked to linger—and the extreme Seicento art of Florence and Sicily was a favourite—were swept out. Only the 'great' Baroque artists, Annibale, Caravaggio, Cortona, and the classic Bolognese whose excesses were sanctioned by generations of admiring collectors were worthy of study. While Berenson encouraged admiration of painters so obscure that their only identity lay in some slight similarity to another, more positive—but still anonymous—master, only a few art historians such as Hermann Voss, Matteo Marangoni and Roberto Longhi had the courage to admire and study the painters of Florence's "forgotten centuries". It is their pupils and admirers who have laid the foundations of serious study of this neglected period.

Although the major Florentine collections of the Uffizi and the Pitti contain some of the finest examples of paintings from this period, it is nevertheless not easy to study the painters represented in this exhibition. Many of their best works are in private collections, and since interest in their altarpieces is very recent indeed, a depressingly small number of the many still *in situ* in Tuscan churches have been rescued from their centuries-old layers of dirt. A supreme effort of the imagination is necessary to visualize what many of such paintings originally looked like, but to judge by the brilliant colouring of the one major altarpiece in this exhibition (No. 4)—recently cleaned by the National Gallery—their effect in even the darkest interiors must have been considerable. The very nature of much of the period's favourite subject-matter has led to the specialisation by certain collectors (notably in Florence) in the more extreme examples of the macabre, the *recherché* or the bizarre: the taste for such excesses in Seicento painting is scarcely known, let alone understood in this country, which has a tradition of adhering to the more classic, or at least restrained, examples. The rarity of superb Florentine Seicento paintings also ensures that the vogue for them can never reach the proportions of a 'revival', and any study of them *en masse* can only be made in exhibitions such as this.

Four principal studies of the historical background to this exhibition exist to enrich the visitor's enjoyment of the often confusingly complex events in later Medici history. They are Gaetano Pieraccini's monumental *La Stirpe de' Medici di Cafaggiolo*, Colonel G. F. Young's *The Medici* (1909), Sir Harold Acton's *The Last Medici*, first published in 1932, and Eric Cochrane's *Florence in the Forgotten Centuries 1527-1800* of 1974. So far, no general study of Florentine 17th century art has appeared, although two major contributions in English together provide an outline: Joan Nissman and Howard Hibbard's catalogue of the exhibition *Florentine Baroque Art from American Collections* held at the Metropolitan Museum in New York in 1969, and the exhibition catalogue of *The Twilight of the Medici* (Detroit-Florence, 1974).

In what he described as his "chronicle of decadence"—*The Last Medici*, Sir Harold Acton coined a memorable phrase which crystallises both Florentine life and art in the 17th century: "the sublime and the vile touched hands". A glance at the pictures in this exhibition show how true this was. In one mood, the genius of the early part of the century, Cristofano Allori could immortalise the penetratingly intelligent gaze of a remarkable friend (No. 2) and in another, wallow in the depths of symbolic self-degradation (No. 1). Carlo Dolci, capable of images of extraordinary purity (Nos 18, 20) increasingly turned away from reality to release from his imagination those creatures of crystalline perfection who seem to exist perpetually in a twilight world of tears and self-mortification (Nos. 15, 18). While Cesare Dandini's pallid somnambulists resolutely refuse to acknowledge the existence of feeling (Nos. 12, 13), the necrophiliac heroine of the painter-priest Francesco Furini revels in her private orgy of conflicting emotions (No. 30). The dichotomy which reveals itself in almost every aspect of Florentine culture of the period is essentially that of the individual snared against his will by the machinery of a state hopeful of imposing on him beliefs it does not personally hold.

While Papal Rome in the 17th century offered its faithful some of the most spectacular diversions ever seen in Western society—and petrified others in the masterpieces of Bernini and Borromini—later Medici Florence never attempted to turn itself into a Baroque city. The result was that the spectacular piety of the Grand Duchess Vittoria della Rovere (always most in evidence on the rebound from her equally spectacular bouts of spendthrift frivolity) must have seemed to her subjects like the golden rain from rockets which vanishes when it touches the ground. Contrary to what is usually said, the deeply pious imagery of Dolci—one of the Grand Duchess's favourite artists—was created in spite of, not because of, her particular type of bigoted religiosity.

Vittoria della Rovere had been brought up in Florence by the *Serenissimi Tutrici*, Maria Maddalena of Austria, wife of the Grand Duke Cosimo II (1590-1620) and his mother Christina of Lorraine, who appear on either side of Cosimo II's young son Ferdinando in No. 52. Vittoria had been groomed by the two women to marry Ferdinando II, and throughout his reign (1620-70) her limited intelligence must always have seemed at odds with that of her highly intelligent and cultivated husband: she won the battle however for the mind of their son Cosimo, who was born in 1642 and reigned from 1670-1723. His failure as a husband (to Louis XIV's neice Marguerite Louise d'Orleans in 1663) and as a ruler, hastening the downfall of his dynasty, can be laid almost entirely at his mother's door. But the process had begun the Regency of the *Tutrici* from 1620-27. By the time when, paradoxically, many of the painters represented in this exhibition such as Furini, Dandini, Lorenzo Lippi, Simone Pignoni, Jacopo Vignali, Volterrano, Sustermans and Dolci, were first emerging as individual artists, (roughly speaking around 1630) the detrimental effects of the regency on Tuscan life was being felt. In 1620, Florence had an estimated 4,000 monks: by the end of the century that number rose to more than 10,000. This might have been expected to have a beneficial effect on the arts, multiplying the number of new churches and commissions for paintings and sculpture on an unprecedented scale. On the contrary, few new churches of any architectural importance were built in Florence—Silvani's S. Gaetano of 1645 looks hopelessly outdated beside a contemporary Roman building—and the largest ecclesiastical fresco, Volterrano's SS. Annunziata *Coronation of the Virgin* of 1681-3 appears in a much older church.

The death of Cristofano Allori in 1621 represents a natural *caesura* in Florentine painting. He had added an element previously noticeably lacking in Florentine counter-Mannerist painting—genius, and had he had greater strength of character and lived longer he might have occupied Matteo Rosselli's place as *caposcuola*. As it was, Cigoli, who found every important Florentine commission in the 1590's snapped up by Santi di Tito or Passignano to the extent that he painted mainly away from the city, gave up and left for greater things in Rome in 1604. Rosselli (1578-1650) inherited the naturalistic tradition begun by Santi di Tito's *Nativity* of 1564 (Florence, S. Giuseppe) in opposition to current Mannerist trends, but lacked the technique and imagination of Jacopo da Empoli (No. 6, 7) and was most important as a teacher: his pupils included Giovanni da San Giovanni (No. 35, 36), Furini, Vignali (Nos. 54, 55), Lorenzo Lippi (Nos. 31, 32, 33), Volterrano (Nos. 28, 29), and their biographer Filippo Baldinucci (q.v.). The subtlety of Allori's art, and his "sustained mood of introspection" (Chappell) were far in advance of painters like Rosselli, and were to have an immense influence on the next generation. Cosimo II's death one year prior to Allori's also brought abruptly to an end a short-lived but intense period of artistic development. Although Florentine painters (Sigismondo Coccapani (1583-1642), Biliverti (see No. 4), Rosselli and Allori) had been in Rome in the early years of the century, the first major impact of Caravaggism was felt with the visits of Artemesia Gentileschi between 1613-20 and of Battistello Caracciolo in 1617 at Cosimo II's invitation. Cosimo went as far as to commission from Caracciolo a portrait of the Grand Duchess, which, although lost, represented a major step forward in the patronage of Caravaggio's followers. In 1620, Cosimo negotiated for the purchase of paintings by Honthorst, four of which entered the Medici collections shortly afterwards. The influence of all of this was neither immediate nor obvious, but certainly without Caravaggism (as distinct from *Caravaggio*) paintings such as Nos. 33 are inconceivable in Florence. Cosimo's reign also saw the presence in Florence of the French engraver of fantastic and often macabre scenes, Jacques Callot, between 1611-21. The precise effect of Callot's prints is hard to estimate, but Giovanni da San Giovanni's nervous, bright figures and scenes like No. 35 owe much to them.

The major decorative schemes of the later 16th and early 17th centuries in Florence are ecclesiastical frescoes, such as the colourful and underrated cloister lunettes in the SS. Annunziata and S. Marco by Rosselli, Poccetti and others. Although one painter who came to maturity in the 1630's, Giovanni Martinelli (see Nos. 37, 38) began his career with such frescoes, after 1610 the most important decorative complexes are secular, either mythological or historical. Four of these are important in assessing the standing and styles of the artists involved at particular times; the Casa Buonarroti, decorated mainly between 1615 and 1620 for Michelangelo Buonarroti the Younger (1568-1646) by a team of painters including Artemesia Gentileschi, Giovanni da San Giovanni, Biliverti, Empoli, Rosselli, Passignano, Crostofano Allori, Vignali, Tarchiani and Curradi, is perhaps the best place to study each of these artists in a semi-official role. This was followed by the group of paintings of 1622-3 for the Casino Mediceo by Cesare Dandini, Rosselli, Curradi, Vignali, Empoli, Passignano and, curiously, Lanfranco and the Sienese Rutilio Manetti. Manetti and his compatriot Rustici also figured in the scheme of 1623-5 for the Audience Chamber at the Grand Duchess Maria Maddalena's Villa of Poggio Imperiale with Curradi and Rosselli. The theme of this room, with its ten fresco lunettes showing episodes from the lives of Royal female saints and four canvases of women famous in Antiquity for their moral or civil virtue (Lucretia, Sophonisba, Artemesia, Semiramis) had particular importance for such painters as Furini, Pignoni and Ficherelli who later used these subjects extensively.

The dynastic aspirations reflected in such a choice of themes dated back to Cosimo, 1st Grand Duke of Tuscany (1519-74) and reach their real artistic climax in the last important fresco cycle painted by Florentines in the 17th century, the decoration of the *Sala terrena* (now Museo degli Argenti) in the Pitti Palace, commissioned from Giovanni da San Giovanni in 1635 to celebrate the forthcoming marriage of Ferdinando II with Vittoria della Rovere. These frescoes show a group of allegories connected with Lorenzo the Magnificent, and significantly, Rosselli was not among the painters asked to complete the room after Giovanni's death in 1636: Ferdinando's sights were aiming higher, and Pietro da Cortona's arrival in Florence in 1637 *en route* for Venice suddenly made even the *Sala terrena* appear stilted. Cortona's frescoes in the Pitti Palace's Sala della Stufa were intended as an allegory of the return of another Golden Age with the Medici-della Rovere alliance, but for Florentine painters they only marked the end of hopes of Grand Ducal patronage for important decorative schemes. Turning to Curradi, Rosselli is reputed to have said before Cortona's frescoes, "How small the rest of us are." It was however this very smallness, and in general the ensuing tendency of the Florentines to concentrate on smaller private commissions which resulted in many of their most characteristic and beautiful pictures.

The effects of Cortona's Pitti work of 1637 and 1640-47 (the Planetary Rooms) are scarcely visible in this exhibition, although Volterrano's *Hylas* (No. 29) and Pietro Dandini's *Allegory of Painting* (No. 14) are obviously indebted. As for Luca Giordano's longest visits to the city in 1582 and 1585 when he painted the Corsini Chapel in the Church of the Carmine and the vast, brilliant ceiling of the Medici-Riccardi Palace—these are reflected in the exhibition's latest works, Pignoni's *Allegory* (No. 47) and Sagrestani's *Pieta with Angels* (No. 49).

Too much attention has perhaps been paid to the *quadri da stanza* into which the native Florentines of the period *c.* 1620-1690 poured their creative energy in the absence of larger commissions such as were found in Rome or Bologna. Most of the painters shown here also painted altarpieces of some importance. Cigoli, Allori, Empoli, Vignali, Tarchiani, Dolci, Lippi, Pignoni and Ficherelli have all been judged largely on the strength of their secular or smaller religious commissions, but until methodical study of their larger ecclesiastical works is made, the image of the period will remain limited. Although Florence did not provide the countless new altars found in Rome after the Counter-Reformation, a new religious iconography certainly arose. It was, after all Florence which gave Italy two of its most important Counter-Reformation saints, S. Caterina de' Ricci (1522-90) and S. Maria Maddalena de' Pazzi (1566-1607) both of whom provided Florence with ample material for new imagery. The Papacy's greatly increased interest in Early Christian themes during the Counter-Reformation found eager acceptance in Florence, where apart from local saints like St. Zenobius (No. 4) finding obvious popular audiences, a saint such as St. Praxedis (No. 45) accorded perfectly with Florentine taste for the ambiguous or macabre. More than in any other Italian city, Old Testament stories were favoured at Florence (Nos. 10, 22, 26, 55), and Florentine painters in the 17th century still clung to their predecessors' favourites such as the Magdalen and David (Nos. 15, 34 and 24).

Since the study of the period as a whole is still in its infancy, few attempts have been made to relate the social history of the Seicento in Tuscany to its art. Events of shattering importance such as the Plague of 1630, which carried off the young and promising Bartolomeo Salvestrini, must have affected the rising generation of painters, and its influence can be seen possibly in two different ways: on the one hand, painters like Lippi and Martinelli developed their strongly realistic styles in its wake, possibly in reaction to the tendencies towards increasing luxuriance in painting which appeared during the second decade of the century. The very young Carlo Dolci, highly susceptible as he was to every outward symbol of human transience, was painting his first religious works at precisely the same period, and there can be no doubt that the more vigorous style of Cristofano Allori, early Biliverti and Matteo Rosselli of the 1620's gives way increasingly after 1630 to greater introspection. The unwelcome arrival of Pietro da Cortona in 1637 probably had little more immediate effect than to turn artists such as Curradi, Dolci or Vignali even more pronouncedly against the advancing tide of the Baroque, increasing their instinctive dislike of such extroversion. It is too easy to presume that the sudden appearance of an avant-garde painter in a provincial art scene should engender immediate and unhesitating servitude on the part of local artists, and an examination of many of the paintings here proves that their resistance was strong.

The traditionalism fostered by Grand Ducal nostalgia for Florence's greatest period, the 15th century, found direct reflection in painting. Although an artist such as Empoli can be said to have been partly a survival of early 16th century ideas (see No. 6) the many copies made by him, his pupil Ficherelli (see Nos. 26, 27) and others including Lupicini (see No. 34) and Ottavio Vannini of much earlier masters indicates a strongly revivalist urge which is directly reflected in their paintings. Dolci too deliberately evoked fifteenth century and even earlier art (see No. 18). This chauvinistic element in much painting of the period adds to its fascination, and was also vitally linked to the nascent conception of Florence as a gigantic museum of the Medici and their treasures: in 1602 the Florentine Accademia del Disegno was asked to supervise the imposition of a law forbidding the export of works of art by famous masters of the past including Michelangelo, Raphael and Bronzino. But chauvinism was not the sole reason for studying earlier painters, and Dandini (see Nos. 00, 00) together with others like Mario Balassi extensively copied Dürer's style.

Apart from No. 52 the paintings shown here reflect little of Grand Ducal taste. Practically no research has been carried out into private patronage during this period, although the exhibition *La Quadreria di Don Lorenzo de' Medici* (Poggio a Caiano, 1977) made interesting overtures in that direction. Pictures painted for the Bostichi, Venturi, del Rosso, Lorenzo, Rinuccini, del Sera, Grazini, Riccardi, and del Turco families are included in the exhibition. Many of these had collections of varying sizes and importance, but almost nothing is known as yet of their taste or patronage. As the visitor to the exhibition will see, some of the paintings were already in England in the 17th century (Nos. 19, 21), while others were bought in the following century either as a result of apparently rather advanced discrimination (Nos. 10, 26, 31), misattribution to better-known artists (Nos. 55, 27) or simply through the fame of the painter (Nos. 23, 25). As the paintings of Guercino, Reni, Domenichino, Cortona, Rosa and others so admired and studied by our ancestors increasingly find their final, well-documented resting places in museums, these pictures may be the subject of merited, but long-overdue attention and admiration.

I wish to express my gratitude to Messrs. P. & D. Colnaghi for mounting this exhibition, and to all those who have assisted me during its preparation and cataloguing:

Prof. Luigi Baldacci, Dr. Anna Barsanti, Prof. Piero Bigongiari, Dr. Evelina Borea, Dr. Giuseppe Cantelli, Dr. Miles Chappel, Dr. Marco Chiarini, Dr. Andrew Ciechanowiecki, Mr. Michael Goedhuis, Prof. Mina Gregori, Mr. Leslie Harris, Dr. Christoph Heilmann, Mr. Rupert Hodge, Prof. Michael Jaffé, Prof. Herbert Keutner, Dr. Rolf Kultzen, Prof. Mario Montuori, Mr. Philip Pouncey, Miss Jane Rick, Dr. Stella Rudolph, Prof. John Shearman, Mr. Malcolm Waddingham and the staffs of the National Art Library at the Victoria and Albert Museum, and the Kunsthistorisches Institut, Florence. I also wish to thank the various lenders who have permitted me to study their collections prior to the exhibition, and Mr. Clovis Whitfield of Colnaghi's, who undertook the organisation of the exhibition. The exhibition would have been impossible without his energy and enthusiasm. Mrs. Pamela Grundy and Miss Ursula Lanz, also of Colnaghi's gave invaluable assistance with many problems.

Charles McCorquodale

CATALOGUE

CRISTOFANO ALLORI
1577-Florence-1621

The son of the late Mannerist painter Alessandro Allori (1535-1607) Allori was often referred to by his family name, Bronzino, after his father's uncle. Baldinucci noted that "his works, though rare, are wonderful beyond belief" and Allori was already referred to as *famosissimo* in 1616. Noting with distaste Alessandro's "hard manner", Baldinucci tells us that Cristofano reacted against it by entering the studio of Gregorio Pagani (1558-1605) whom he admired together with Cigoli and Santi di Tito: Allori's conversion to a more modern manner is symbolically documented in his *Miracle of the Blessed Manetti* (1602, Florence, SS. Annunziata) where he portrayed himself as the boy being cured while his father and other artists look on. His perfectionism (see No. 3) was already apparent in his earliest works, and the SS. Annunziata painting made his reputation in Florence. The psychological insight of his portraits (see No. 2) appears also in his other paintings such as *The Hospitality of St. Julian*, (Florence, Pitti), *The Madonna giving the Rosary to St. Dominic* (Pistoia, S. Domenico) and notably his celebrated *Judith* (see No. 1), long considered the major masterpiece of the Florentine 17th century. A Roman journey in 1610 introduced him to Caravaggio's larger paintings, and the presence of Artemesia Gentileschi in Florence may also have influenced his treatment of the pictorial 'values' which was to exercise such widespread influence on native Florentines. Allori was a fine landscapist, as we know from many surviving drawings, and like several other Florentine artists of the period was also an accomplished poet and musician.

His noted capriciousness, whose effects on his studio caused several of his pupils such as Zanobi Rosi and Cesare Dandini to leave, may partly account for the scarcity of his paintings, his last major work was *Michelangelo in Meditation* (1621, Florence, Casa Buonarotti) and after his terrible death from gangrene in a foot, several works were finished by pupils.

1   *Judith with the Head of Holofernes*

Oil on canvas, 120.4 by 100.3cms. Signed and dated 1613

PROVENANCE: The picture was certainly in the Royal Collection by the time of Queen Anne; it is possible that it had belonged to the Gonzaga collection acquired by Charles I in 1627.

LITERATURE: Baldinucci, 1846, III, pp. 726–728; Law, 1898 p. 109; Collins Baker, 1929, p. 1; Shearman, 1979, pp. 2-10, repr. (colour) frontispiece.

The Apocryphal Book of Judith tells how the beautiful Jewish widow Judith seduced the Assyrian commander Holofernes, and on one of her nightly visits to his tent succeeded in decapitating him with his sword during his drunken sleep. Baldinucci recounts how Allori, having submitted to the mortifications advocated by the devotional *compagnia* of the Blessed Ippolito Galantini in apparent remorse for earlier excesses, suddenly renounced them and, coincidentally, fell in love with "a certain beautiful woman called La Mazzafirra". He spent recklessly on her, but appears to have obtained nothing but misery from the liaison. The only positive result was a portrait of his mistress as Judith holding his head in the guise of Holofernes, watched by La Mazzafirra's mother.

Shearman (op. cit.) suggests that Allori's mistress may be identifiable as Maria di Giovanni Mazzafirri, who died in 1617, and that the later version in the Pitti Palace shows a different model. No. 1 is the only version of the many in existence which is inscribed and dated: Shearman (op. cit.) provides the following translation of the inscription painted in shell-gold on the bed beneath the green mattress: "This (work is) of Cristoforo Allori Bronzino; hitherto unvanquished, (she) has almost been defeated by the labour (of) painting, in the year 1613". Presumably this refers to the artist's problems with his mistress. While it has now been proved that the Pitti version (which is slightly larger) has nothing to do with a version painted for Cardinal Orsini (Pizzorusso, 1978), there remains a possibility that No. 1 was the one whose delivery to the Cardinal Allori repeatedly delayed: Shearman suggests that it may have been on account of the matter being placed before the Grand Duke that the latter ordered other versions from the artist. The equally complex problem of the many related studies for the picture is also summarized by Shearman, who points out that several of them are specifically for this initial version.

The brilliantly assured handling of paint and colour in No. 1 (despite the countless changes made by Allori throughout the painting) together with the infinite subtlety in conveying Judith's expression distinguishes this earlier version from that in the Pitti, whose heavier, jaded expression led de Musset to describe her as "cette fausse Judith"—a *double entendre* both on the original heroine's patriotic use of her charms and on La Mazzafirra's much less altruistic use of hers. Shearman's suggestion that, because La Mazzafirra died in 1617 Allori chose not to paint the likeness of the dead woman in the later version(s) of the picture, may well account for the fact that No. 1 is clearly a lively portrait while the Pitti painting is more generalized and ideal. The acceptance of No. 1 as Allori's prime original (Law and Collins Baker, *op. cit.* both regarded it as a copy) leads to a revaluation not only of the chronological importance of the Mazzafirra affair in Allori's life, but also of his precise attitude to his mistress, who here appears younger and fresher than the Pitti version had led Allori's critics to imagine her.

Pizzorusso (1978) draws attention to a letter written from Paris by the poet Giambattista Marino during his stay there from 1615-23, in which he says that Allori's *Judith* was already popular in Paris.

Her Majesty the Queen.

2   *Portrait of Bernardo Davanzati Bostichi*

Oil on canvas, 48 by 36cm.

PROVENANCE: Bostichi family, Florence; Incontri family, Florence; Eyre (?); Lord Nelson
LITERATURE: Baldinucci, 1846, III, p. 723; Cambiagi, 1769-75, IX, p. 14; National Art Collection Fund Annual Report, 1951, p. 33, repr; Ashmolean Annual Report, 1951, p. 55, repr; Oxford, 1961, pp. 12-13; Ewald, 1965, p. 306, and fig. 10; Del Bravo, 1967 (a), p. 69 and note 1, repr. fig. 39;

Bernardo Davanzati Bostichi (1529-1606), "the Florentine Tacitus", was a noted Classical scholar, whose translations of Tacitus into concise Italian received wide acclaim. Ugo Foscolo called his rendering of Dante into contemporary Florentine "the most marvellous ever made". Bostichi translated the English Jesuit Nicolas Sanders' *History of the English Schism* from Latin, and wrote treatises on commerce and viti-culture. Principally noted for the terseness of his style—in contrast to the verbosity of his contemporaries—he was admitted to the Accademia degli Alterati with the pseudonym *The Silent* and was made Consul of the Accademia Fiorentina in 1575. He was also involved in the Accademia della Crusca's preparation of the famous *Vocabolario*.

Baldinucci describes two portraits by Allori of Bernardo Davanzati Bostichi, this and another "of more than half length", which was presumably the one later in the collection of the connoisseur Nicolò Gaburri (Gaburri, 1739, II, p. 568). In stating that the latter was painted in 1610, Baldinucci was either unaware of the date of Bostichi's death, or was confusing the portrait with that of Bernardo's son Carlo. Although Baldinucci does not specifically mention a portrait of Carlo, he says that Allori painted for him a portrait of a young man with a collar "all'antica": Gambiagi (op. cit.) mentions a portrait of ". . . Carlo . . . in his youth, with a collar 'all'antica', which was taken to England." Since Gambiagi was writing in the later 1760's, it is likely that he too was confusing the portraits of father and son, and was in fact referring to the portrait of Bernardo which seems to have been in England by that date.

The portrait is one of the most striking likenesses of the early Baroque, and its sense of intimacy may arise from the close friendship between the artist and the Bostichi, to which Baldinucci refers (Allori was himself a poet of some stature (Rosini, 1846)). Although its realism may owe something to Allori's knowledge of Barocci—whose landscape drawings certainly appear to have influenced him (Del Bravo, op. cit.)—the chiaroscuro recalls Empoli, and indicates the extent to which Caravaggism had filtered into Florentine painting long before the arrival of Artemesia Gentileschi. Presumably painted shortly before Bostichi's death at the age of 77, it compares in style with the portraits of Michelangelo the Younger, Alessandro Allori, Gregorio Pagani and others in Allori's *Miracle of the Beato Manetto* of 1602 in the SS. Annunziata at Florence (Chappell, 1977 (a)). The vivacity of Allori's portrait drawings and small likenesses on copper (Del Bravo, op. cit.) has no rivals among his Florentine contemporaries, and Baldinucci says that the beauty of another portrait on copper of Maddalena Scarlatti Bostico was "the wonder of that era".

Visitors of the Ashmolean Museum, Oxford.

3 *St. Francis of Assisi in Prayer*

Oil on copper, 40 by 30cms.

Baldinucci says that Allori painted "the beautiful painting of the kneeling St. Francis in prayer" for his doctor, Zerbinelli. He hired a Capuchin friar as his model "solely for the retouching of one of the eyes" so great was his desire for perfection. The original evidently enjoyed great esteem in early 17th century Florence: Chappell (1971) maintains that the original by Allori is that in the Casa Vasari at Arezzo (panel, 46 by 36cm.) and that Allori "made larger and smaller replicas of it at different times in his career." This would appear to be one of these versions. Apart from those noted by Chappell, a fine version is in the Weld Collection, and another copper attributed to Denys Calvaert is in the Sabauda Gallery, Turin (Gabrielli, 1971), while others by Allori and followers are known.

Chappell has noted the influence of Northern landscape on this group of pictures, and Baldinucci says that Allori imitated the manner of a certain Adriano Fiammingo, who also worked in the Cigoli studio in the early 1600's. Minor variations, notably in the landscape background, distinguish the various versions of the subject: the softness and luminosity of this particular one, together with its emphasis on ecstatic mysticism directly prefigure Carlo Dolci, who made a chalk study of the saint's hands (London, British Museum: Chappel, op. cit. fig. 26). A painting of this theme on copper by Allori ("Bronzino") was in the Gonzaga Collection (Luzio, 1913, p. 121, no. 435).

Ulster Museum, Belfast.

GIOVANNI BILIVERTI

1576-Florence-1644

The son of the Maastricht goldsmith and jeweller Giacomo di Giovanni Bylevelt who probably arrived in Florence shortly before his birth, Biliverti entered the Cigoli studio on the death of his father in 1603. In 1604, he accompanied Cigoli to Rome, where he painted his first known work, *The Martyrdom of S. Callisto* (1604-7) in a style midway between Cigoli's and Caravaggism. The transformation in Cigoli's style in Rome, as represented by his *Joseph and Potiphar's Wife* of 1610 with its sumptuous colour and large figures are reflected in Biliverti's own rendering of the theme of 1611-12 (Florence, Pitti): although no works can be securely connected with the following decade, Biliverti continued in the style of his *Joseph* in *The Finding of the True Cross* (1621, Florence, S. Croce) and *The Angel refusing Tobias's Gifts* of 1622 (Pitti). With the latter, Biliverti moves away from Cigoli towards a softer, more anecdotal style in keeping with other Florentine trends of this period. During the following decade the influence of Matteo Rosselli—then at the height of his success—is felt in Biliverti's work, to be supplanted during the early 1630's by that of Furini, whose *sfumato* style he emulated in his later painting. Apart from Baldinucci's life of Biliverti, his pupil Francesco Bianchi (1603-58) also wrote one, and these in conjunction with a number of dated paintings permit a reconstruction of his chronology. Biliverti's studio produced some of the most interesting painters of the next generation such as Bartolomeo Salvestrini, Baccio del Bianco and Orazio Fidani, each of whom further developed different aspects of their master's style.

4   *St. Zenobius revives a Dead Boy*

Oil on canvas, 205 by 164.4cm.

PROVENANCE: Giuliano Girolami, (?) Florence, George Salting
EXHIBITED: London, British Institution, 1867, No. 22 (as Empoli)
LITERATURE: Bianchi, in Baldinucci, 1975, VII, p. 68; Venturi, 1934, IX, Pt. VII, pp. 668-9
              (as Empoli); Gregori, 1960, p. 106; Ewald, 1965, p. 318, note 13; Levey, 1971,
              pp. 16-17; McCorquodale, 1974, p. 203, repr. fig. 4; Chappell, 1977 (b), p. 68,
              note 3.

The son of pagan parents, St. Zenobius was baptised a Christian by Bishop Theodore. Early biographies differ as to his dates, but he probably died in the second decade of the fifth century in his ninetieth year. He was the legendary first Bishop of Fiesole, and considerable myth accrued around his life and his *Acts*, which cannot in fact have been written before the eleventh century (Cochrane, 1974). No. 4 shows his most famous miracle, which is a fairly common theme in Florentine art (e.g. Domenico Veneziano, Gozzoli and Botticelli). A French woman left her son with the saint while she visited the churches of Rome, but on her return found that the boy had been killed by an ox-cart: St. Zenobius miraculously restored him to life. This occurred in Borgo degli Albizzi near the church of S. Piero Maggiore (in the background of this painting) at a point formerly marked by a stone (Bocchi-Cinelli, 1677). Bilivert's painting constitutes an important record of the appearance of the church prior to the addition in 1638 of the portico by Nigetti. The church was later demolished leaving only the portico.

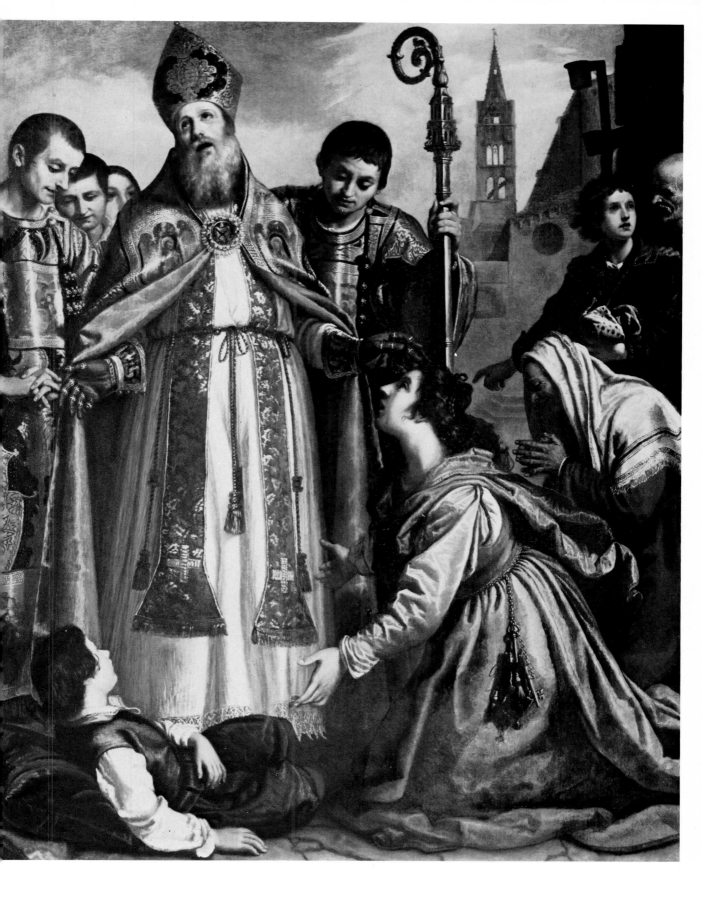

It seems clear that this painting is not the one recorded by Tigri in his *Guida di Pistoia* of 1854 as suggested by Levey (op. cit.): Tolomei, in his guide of 1821 describes the picture by Bilivert in the Sacristy of the Madonna dell'Umiltà at Pistoia as painted in "his second manner", that is to say in the soft, sfumatesque style which Billivert assumed in the early 1630's. A painting of the same theme as No. 4 remains *in situ* in the Sacristy, and is very close in style to Bilivert's "second manner". Furthermore, the measurements of the altar tabernacle— apparently dating from the sixteenth century—do not correspond with those of No. 4. The alternative, mentioned in his life of his master Bilivert by Frencesco Bianchi (op. cit.) is the version of the subject which Bilivert painted for Giuliano Girolami, described by Bianchi as "a large picture". Bianchi appears to follow no chronology in his account, mentioning the painting after Biliverti's *Daniel in the Lions' Den* of 1625 (Pisa, Cathedral) but before the death of the Grand Duke Cosimo II (1621). A dating between 1620-22 seems acceptable for stylistic reasons: the painting is transitional between *Michelangelo and the Ambassadors* of 1616-20 (Florence, Casa Buonarroti) and *The Angel refusing Tobias's Gifts* of 1622 (Florence, Pitti). Several of the models used in No. 4 appear also in Bilivert's *Finding of the True Cross* of 1621 (Florence, S.Croce) in which St. Helena is not only painted from the same model as the mother in this painting, but is seen in an almost identical pose. The boy at the extreme right appears in a drawing in the Uffizi (G.D.S.U. 2075.S) and may have been the model in *Joseph and Potiphar's Wife* of 1611-12 (Florence, Pitti). Characteristic of Bilivert at this period is the meticulous attention to the differentiation of pictorial values—the luxurious robes of the saint and his two deacons SS. Eugenius and Crescentius, the brilliant white linens and the carefully-distinguished old and young flesh. Chappell (*op. cit.*) suggests that a number of Florentine paintings of "revival" themes like that of No. 4, derive from Cigoli.

LODOVICO CARDI, *called* IL CIGOLI   1559 Castelvecchio di Cigoli-1613 Rome

Cigoli is one of the key figures in the transformation of Florentine painting from late Mannerism to the early Baroque, and although he left Florence to live in Rome in 1604, his previous work and his contacts with Florentine artists in Rome continued to be influential. Apart from Baldinucci, Giovanni Battista Cardi, the artist's nephew, and Giovanni Baglione wrote biographies of him. Cigoli's earliest training is obscure, but after four years in Alessandro Allori's studio, he returned to his birthplace to recover from an illness. Thus the first influences on his style were those on the whole of Florentine Mannerism at its most extreme. After further study with the architect Bernardo Buontalenti (1536-1608) and Santi di Tito (1536-1603) who probably introduced him to a closer study of the model, Cigoli began to make use of his experiences of non-Florentine art. Like Annibale Carracci in Bologna, Cigoli was attracted to Correggio, Barocci and the Venetians, and their influence is first seen in his paintings of the 1590's such as *The Martyrdom of St. Stephen* of 1597 (one of the most fully Baroque of Florentine pictures), *The Miracle of the Mule* of the same year (Cortona, S. Francesco) and the deeply Correggesque *Pietà* of 1599 (Vienna, Kunsthistorisches Museum). His warm, sensuous colour and atmospherics and his devotion to rich fabrics were also very influential on Florentine art during the next fifty years. At the same time as Barocci, Cigoli was also experimenting with themes like *The Ecstasy of St. Francis* (Florence, Uffizi), and *Ecce Homo* (Pitti) whose intense emotionalism is echoed in Vignali and Dolci.

Cigoli's impact on Roman painting may have been greater than has been realised, and he continued his work as an architect there. His *Joseph and Potiphar's Wife* painted in 1610 for Cardinal Scipione Borghese (Rome, Borghese Gallery) sums up many of his later aims and achievements.

24

5 *The Dream of Jacob*

Oil on canvas 150.5 by 130cms.

PROVENANCE: Cardinal Montalto (?), Rome

LITERATURE: G. B. Cardi, 1913, pp. 22, 26; Burghley Catalogue, 1954, No. 58; Thiem, 1977 (b), p. 290, No. 37 and fig. 254.

The story of Jacob's dream is told in Genesis, XXVIII: 10-15. On his journey from Beersheba to Haran, Jacob stopped to rest and dreamt that he saw angels ascending and descending a ladder to heaven. God appeared at the top of the ladder and promised Jacob's inheritance.

Baldinucci (1846, III, p. 247) noted that Cigoli painted a picture of this theme for Cosimo Ridolfi which then passed into the collection of Cardinal Carlo de' Medici: this is probably the version in the Musée des Beaux Arts, Nancy which is signed and dated 1593 (Brunetti, 1959). Cardi (op. cit.) says that Cigoli subsequently painted a second version for Cardinal Montalto at Rome, and this is probably No. 5. A study for the whole composition is in the Gabinetto Nazionale delle Stampe, Rome, and other studies are in the Uffizi (Thiem, op. cit.). The composition, which derives from Raphael's rendering in the Vatican Loggie, exercised considerable influence in Florence, reappearing notably in a small copper attributed to Rosselli in the Corsini Gallery, in Vignali's fresco in the Casa Buonarroti (Procacci, 1965), and modified, in a painting attributed to Cristofano Allori in the Galleria Sabauda, Turin (Gabrielli, 1971). There are only minimal differences between the two versions.

Painted in the 1590's when Cigoli was most under the influence of Correggio, the colour-scheme, treatment of costume and the generally romantic air of the main figure—together with the softness in the paint handling and the landscape—can all be regarded as prefiguring many features of Florentine 17th century painting (see Nos. 7, 8, 25, 30). The theatricality of Jacob's pose has been noted by several writers.

The Marquess of Exeter.

JACOPO CHIMENTI, *called* JACOPO DA EMPOLI   1551-Florence-1640

Empoli's painting represents not only a reaction to the Mannerism of Vasari (died 1574) and his school, but, more significantly, a deliberate return to the values of the Florentine High Renaissance and early *Maniera* as represented by Andrea del Sarto, Fra' Bartolomeo and the young Pontormo. He trained under Maso da San Friano (died 1571), who, although he lacked the real reforming zeal of Santi di Tito (1536-1603) or Bernardino Poccetti (1548-1612) was at least representative of the first moves towards greater naturalism. Empoli ceaselessly studied and copied Pontormo (including the entire series of Certosa frescoes) and Sarto, whose widow he knew. For Cardinal Carlo de' Medici, Empoli copied Fra Bartolomeo's Pitti *Resurrection* then in the SS. Annunziara. These copies are of the highest quality, and Empoli passed on his talent as a copyist to his pupil Felice Ficherelli. In 1576 he registered with the Accademia del Disegno, and his *Immaculate Conception* of 1591 (Florence, S. Remigio) shows that although his style was almost independent of Mannerist formulae, it was different from the 'reformed' painting of Cigoli. His *Toilet of Susanna* of 1600 (Vienna, Kunthistorisches Museum) shows the essence of his style, from which he did not vary considerably later—formal clarity, strong, clear colour, naturalistically-observed gesture and detail, and forms of monumental simplicity. His masterpiece of the 'teens, *St. Charles Borromeo with the Rospigliosi Family* (1613, Pistoia, S. Domenico)

shows his interest in minutely accurate costume-detail which probably exerted considerable influence on Biliverti and his pupils (see No. 4). An increased sense of scale fills his *Madonna and Saints* of 1628 (Florence, SS. Annunziata) which also shows a strong dependence on the early 16th century.

Empoli was also a still-life painter and portraitist of distinction, and worked on festival decorations for the Medici and in the Casa Buonarroti. Apart from Baldinucci, there is a manuscript life of Empoli by his pupil Virginio Zaballi in the National Library at Florence.

6   *The Adoration of the Shepherds*

Oil on panel, 83.3 by 66.1cms.

PROVENANCE: Charles Rogers, by 1768
LITERATURE: McCorquodale, 1979 (b).

According to Luke, II: 15-16, the shepherds of Judaea, having been told by angels of the birth of Christ in Bethlehem, hurried there and found the Holy Family with the Child lying in a manger.

This altarpiece is a highly important addition to Empoli's *oeuvre*, documenting his artistic beginnings under the influence of his master Maso da San Friano and of Santi di Tito and Poccetti. Although the poses still evoke the pictorial devices of Florentine Mannerism (going back as far as Bronzino's *Adoration* in Budapest of the 1530's), these are tempered by a strong naturalism which is particularly evident in the preparatory studies in the Uffizi (McCorquodale, *op. cit.* figs. 2, 3). Anna Forlani dated the preparatory drawing for the whole composition (Uffizi 9281 F: Forlani, 1962) to 1570-80, noting in particular the smoothly-rounded face of the Virgin as prefiguring Empoli's later manner: the finished panel closely follows this drawing with only slight variations such as the inclusion of fewer angels and one less shepherd, and confirms Forlani's dating of the drawing. The original location of the painting—which was presumably an altarpiece—is unknown, but in view of its modest dimensions, it may be the picture of this theme recorded as having been painted for the pork-butcher Luca Salesi (Forlani, *op. cit.*).

Empoli appears to have liked this composition, re-using elements of both its composition and detail in his later *Nativity* in S. Michele Visdomini, Florence. A studio variant based on No. 6 is in the National Gallery of Ireland, Dublin.

No. 6 is the earliest work in the exhibition, and shows clearly the beginnings of the straight-forward narrative style which Empoli later developed with increased sophistication, and which continued to exert considerable influence on Florentine painters even after his death.

Plymouth, City Museum and Art Gallery.

7   *Portrait of Concino Concini*

Oil on canvas, 208.1 by 134.5 cms. Inscribed, top left: 'ANNO AETATIS SUAE XXXXI'

PROVENANCE: Otto Messinger, Munich: Baron Fassini, Rome
LITERATURE: Venturi, 1913, pp. 141-5, repr. fig. 1
EXHIBITED: Florence, Palazzo Vecchio, 1911, *Mostra del Ritratto Italiano*, p. 206, No. 6

Concino Concini (1569-1617) was a Florentine who went to France in the train of Maria de' Medici on the occasion of her marriage to Henry IV. In 1610 he became First Gentleman-in-Waiting to the Queen and in the same year purchased the Marquisate of Ancres. He later obtained successive governorships of Amiens and of Normandy and a Marshall's baton (*Marechale d'Ancre*). He exercised immense influence over the Queen to the anger of many, and on his being declared of age in 1614, Louis XIII planned to dispose of him. Concini was arrested on the Pont du Louvre in 1617 and murdered by the King's Guards. His wife Leonora Galigai was siezed shortly afterwards and burned at the stake for sorcery. Concini's brother Bartolomeo appears in No. 52.

With reference to the inscription in the upper left of the canvas ("in his 41st year"), Concini was 41 in 1610, and it is likely that this portrait was painted to commemorate the successful events of that year. The inscription on the letter in his right hand reads "Alla Maestà Christianissima della Regina di Francia Maria di Medici 1600", and refers to the Queen's accession, not to the date of the picture. Venturi (*op. cit.*) claims that a portrait of Concini appears in *Christ at Emmaus* (Munich, Alte Pinakothek) formerly attributed to Empoli and now tentatively given to Tarchiani (see No. 53).

Few portraits by Empoli are known, and their attributions are based entirely on stylistic comparison with his other work. Baldinucci makes no reference to this portrait, although he does mention a "stupendous portrait" of Concini in bust-length by Cigoli, in the Giraldi collection. The attribution to Empoli is traditional and is probably based on the fact that Empoli was responsible for painting *The Marriage of Maria de' Medici and Henry IV*, a studio copy of which is in the collection of the Earl of Elgin.

Private Collection

FRANCESCO CURRADI 1570-Florence-1616

No critical study of Curradi has yet been made, despite his importance as a painter whose style forms a link between Counter-Reformation pictorial simplification and the seventeenth century's demand for visual richness. Baldinucci did not dedicate a life to Curradi, although he is mentioned in those of other painters such as his master, Giovanni Battista Naldini (1537-91) and his pupil Cesare Dandini (see Nos. 10-13). The most comprehensive outline of his activity as a painter is found in Gambiagi (1769-75), which lists more than fifty of his works. Although there are a certain number of dated pictures, Curradi's chronology is difficult to establish since there is little pronounced stylistic change after the 1620's. Curradi entered Naldini's studio after training initially with his father Taddeo, and matriculated in the Accademia del Disegno in 1590. In 1589, he assisted another Naldini pupil, Giovanni Cosci, with the decorations for the ceremonial entry of Cristina of Lorraine into Florence. His earliest paintings closely resemble Naldini's but under the impact of Cigoli, Empoli and Passignano his style evolved rapidly during the 1590's towards simplified narrative compositions using strong colour and rich fabrics: by 1600, the date of his *Madonna of the Rosary with Saints* (Montopoli in Val d'Arno, S. Stefano), the style in which he was thereafter to work was largely formed. Throughout his long life, he continued to receive important commissions such as that for *Fame leading Michelangelo to Immortality* of 1616-17 in the Casa Buonarroti, *Narcissus* of 1622 for Cardinal Carlo de' Medici's Casino di San Marco and *Artemesia* for the Sala dell' Udienza in the Medici villa of Poggio Imperiale in 1623-5. In *c.* 1633, Pope Urban VIII created him a Cavalier of the Order of Christ. Curradi's

few secular paintings deal with tragic themes, and a gentle melancholy pervades his many religious works, which exercised a profound influence on younger painters such as Jacopo Vignali, Bartolomeo Salvestrini and Carlo Dolci. Although he is often at his best in small compositions with few figures, *The Preaching of St. Francis Xavier* (Florence, San Giovannino degli Scolopi) with its exotically costumed crowd has always been considered his masterpiece, while the huge *Virgin in Glory with Saints* (Florence, San Frediano in Cestello) is one of the most important 'classical' Florentine altarpieces of the mid-century. Cesare Dandini studied with Curradi for three years and was used as a model in many of Curradi's paintings.

8   *Tobias and the Angel*

Oil on canvas, 192 by 214.5 cms.

LITERATURE: McCorquodale, 1979(b).

The theme is taken from the Book of Tobias VI, in the Old Testament Apocrypha, and shows the moment when Tobias and his dog, who had been sent on a long journey by his father to collect a debt, encountered the Archangel Raphael by the River Tigris. The Archangel is directing Tobias to catch a fish, which later proved to have miraculous healing powers.

This delightful picture typifies Curradi's art at its most refined and delicate. The simplified, almost relief-like placing of the figures and the precise, highly expressive gesture suggest that Curradi was aware of the type of acting which appears to have characterised the 'sacre rappresentazioni' under the Regency of the Grand Duchesses Christine of Lorraine and Maria Maddalena. His many chalk studies of hands indicate his preoccupation with their significance in heightening the otherwise underplayed drama of his painting: here for example the hands completely express both the Archangel's calm command and Tobias's surprise and uncertainty. While the narrative immediacy recalls Florentine fifteenth century painting and the Archangel's floral robe is strongly reminiscent of Ghirlandaio or Botticelli, the painting's lyrical realism and soft chiaroscuro are wholly of the seventeenth century. Curradi's evolution as a landscape painter of considerable talent remains to be studied, although a signed and dated landscape of 1658 (Gilbert, 1952) shows the influence of Salvator Rosa. Close similarities exist between this landscape and those in his *Narcissus* (Florence, Pitti) and the *Repentent Magdalen* lunette from the Pitti Chapel (Valenti Rodino, 1977). A dating in the 1630's seems acceptable: the close similarity of certain of Carlo Dolci's earliest paintings to the figure of the Archangel underlines Dolci's dependence on Curradi at this time (McCorquodale, 1979(b).)

Although there appears to be no reference to No. 8 in any of the earlier literature on Curradi, a painting of this theme by Curradi is recorded in the Rinuccini Collection in 1842, (Fantozzi, 1842).

Southampton Art Gallery (not shown at Cambridge).

9   *The Toilet of Susanna*

Oil on canvas, 175 by 221 cms. Signed on base of fountain.

PROVENANCE: Woolwich, Royal Military Academy.
LITERATURE: McCorquodale, 1979(b).
EXHIBITED: London, Hazlitt Gallery, 1968, *17th and 18th Century Paintings*, No. 1
ENGRAVED: By B. Eredi, Florence, for Giacomo Moro (as by Matteo Rosselli)

The story of Susanna, beautiful wife of an important Jew during the Babylonian captivity, is told in an apocryphal addendum to the Book of Daniel. Two Elders, attracted by Susanna's beauty, attempted to seduce her after watching her at her toilet. When she rejected them, they denounced her as an adulteress, but Daniel exposed their lies and had them executed.

No. 9 is a fine example not only of Curradi's mature style, but also of the tendency found in Florentine 17th century painting to render such scenes with a note of domestic intimacy. This tendency is at its most pronounced in the work of Rosselli (to whom No. 9 was attributed when the painting was engraved) and Vignali, who generally showed his figures in more or less contemporary Florentine costume regardless of subject-matter. Although the simplified arrangement of figures is reminiscent of Rosselli, the reflective atmosphere together with the full, oval faces framed by braided hair are typical of Curradi. Such faces recur throughout his work, and may be compared with those in *The Virgin in Glory with Saints* (Florence, S. Frediano in Cestello) where all the most characteristic features of his style are in evidence. Curradi's handling of paint as exemplified by the large, smooth drapery folds in this picture, achieves a general softness accentuating the gentle, feminine movements of his figures.

Private Collection.

CESARE DANDINI   1596-Florence-1656

Although Baldinucci devoted a detailed life to Dandini, he was largely ignored by later writers, and only recently has his style begun to be seriously evaluated. At the age of twelve he entered the studio of Francesco Curradi, who, because of Dandini's beauty, "was accustomed to portray him in most of his works." (Baldinucci). Three years later, after an unsatisfactory period with Cristofano Allori, he went to study with Domenico Passignano. His first known work appears to be the *Preaching of St. Vincent Ferrer* in S. Caterina at Pisa, where according to Baldinucci Passignano had taken him as his assistant on work in the Cathedral: his first signed and dated painting is the *Dead Christ with Angels* of 1625 (Florence, SS. Annunziata) whose somewhat laboured execution reveals his uncertain beginnings. Dandini may have gone to Rome and adopted a superficially Caravaggesque style, whose effects surface repeatedly throughout his work in ambiguous and unexpected ways. This may also derive from his contact in Pisa with Riminaldi, and in Florence with Artemesia Gentileschi and Lupicini. By the late 1620's he was working for Don Lorenzo de' Medici, who, aware of Dandini's long-standing passion for Dürer's prints, set him to paint large versions of some of those in his collection. In 1631, Dandini painted two works which show the direction his art was subsequently to follow: *Zerbino and Isabella* for Don Lorenzo (Florence, Gallerie Statali), and *Madonna and Saints* for the SS. Annunziata. In both of these, the 'posed' style of Curradi is transformed into an elegantly artificial theatricality, which Dandini perfected throughout the 1630's to culminate in the hothouse grandeur of his *Diana* (Copenhagen, Statens Museum). Dandini's ventures into Baroque drama, such as the *Conversion of St. Paul* at Vallombrosa and *St. Charles Borromeo in Glory with Saints* in Ancona are not wholly successful, and he is at his best in paintings with a limited number of static figures.

His mask-like faces of deathly pallor with vampirically crimson lips have a suspended, motionless quality midway between Caravaggesque naturalism and the aristocratic aloofness of Bronzino, which led Giovanni da San Giovanni to say that his figures "seemed to be made of glass" (Baldinucci). Cesare's brothers Ottaviano and Vincenzo were both painters as was his nephew, Pietro (see No. 13). Among Dandini's pupils were Stefano della Bella and Alessandro Rosi, whose style is sometimes indistinguishable from his master's.

10 *Moses defending the Daughters of Jethro*

Oil on canvas, 296 by 272 cms.

PROVENANCE: Michelangelo Venturi, Florence: Joseph Leeson, later 1st Earl of Milltown.
LITERATURE: Baldinucci, 1846, IV, pp. 557-558; Bigongiari, 1974, p. 99, note 22, repr. pl. 32; Wynne, 1974, pp. 107-8, repr. pl. 5; Borea, 1975, p. 32 and note 83; Borea 1977, p. 27

Exodus, II, 16-17 recounts how the seven daughters of Jethro, priest of Midian, came to a well to draw water, but were driven away by shepherds. Moses, who had fled into Midian to escape Pharaoh, protected them and was given Jethro's daughter Zipporah in marriage.

One of the masterpieces of the Florentine seventeenth century, this important picture crystallizes many of the principal features of Dandini's mature style. Although Dandini began his career—at least as a draughtsman—in a style closely dependent on Curradi (Thiem 1977(b)), his interest in Florentine Mannerism led to his developing a shorthand graphic style which recalls Pontormo (Bigongiari 1974): like Pontormo he made extensive study of Dürer's prints, and the result is a highly sophisticated synthesis of certain ideas current a century previously. The oval, boneless faces devoid of expression, with their small, full lips and staring eyes evoke the Pontormo of the Certosa frescoes and the S. Felicità *Pietà*, while the flesh tones "with little colour" (Baldinucci) recall the lunar chilliness pervading late Bronzino. Baldinucci describes the picture as having been painted for a certain Michelangelo Venturi, and singles out for particular praise the expression of the '*affetti*' or externalisation of emotion in the figure of Moses. The group of three men is indeed one of the most meticulously observed in Dandini's paintings, and while there are echoes of Curradi's quasi-balletic poses (see No. 8), the metallic brilliance of the draperies—their crisp fluttering folds seemingly frozen in movement—is entirely characteristic of Dandini. No precise dating is yet possible for the painting, but similarities to the *Zerbino and Isabella* and *Erminia and Rinaldo* (Florence, Villa Petraia) suggest that it may date from the period *circa* 1635-45.

A somewhat coarse version, with richer costume and exaggerated facial expressions is in a Florentine private collection.

National Gallery of Ireland, Dublin.

11 *Portrait of a Youth in Armour*

Oil on canvas

LITERATURE: Gregori, 1974, p. 229, note 16

This small canvas appears to be a reduction by Dandini of his sumptuous three-quarter length octagonal canvas showing *The Archangel Michael* (Palermo, Private Collection) published by Carlo Del Bravo (1971, p. 27, repr. fig. 8 in colour). Another version is in the Bigongiari Collection in Florence (Gregori, 1974, p. 221, repr. fig. 7). Unlike these two other versions, this one has no wings or other attributes to suggest a non-secular identification, and there remains the possibility that it prefigures the others. Exceptionally for Dandini, he made a highly finished preparatory study in red chalk for the head (Stuttgart, Staatsgalerie), whose lighting however relates more closely to the Palermo and Bigongiari versions (Gregori, 1974, p. 221,

repr. fig. 8; Thiem, 1977(a) No. 353, p. 186). Although different from the other two in such details as the hand and drapery, and lacking their disturbingly petulant sensuality, this version also conveys the somewhat androgynous ambiguity of the model. The similarity between this model and Curradi's full-length *Archangel Michael* (Sotheby Parke Bernet Sale, New York, 19th September 1974, lot 81, repr.) recalls Baldinucci's statement that many works by Curradi and Dandini were indistinguishable. The strong resemblance of Dandini's figure to that of St. Florian to the right of Guido Reni's *Madonna and Child in Glory with Saints* of 1631-2 (Bologna, Pinacoteca Nazionale) should not be overlooked.

Private Collection.

12   *St. Dorothy of Cappadocia*

Oil on canvas, (octagonal), 119.3 by 99 cms.

LITERATURE: McCorquodale, 1979(b).

St. Dorothy was a Christian girl renowned for her beauty and piety. On her way to martyrdom at the orders of the Governor of Cappadocia, a young lawyer jeered at her, asking her to send him flowers and fruit from paradise. Arriving at the stake, an angel appeared to the saint carrying flowers and fruit, which she sent to the lawyer. He was at once converted to Christianity.

A particularly fine example of Dandini's style at its most characteristic, this painting shows stylistic affinities with Dandini's *Charity* (New York, Metropolitan Museum). The saint's remote and expressionless face, open mouth and elongated fingers together with the modelling of flesh and the still-life of flowers are all typical of Dandini's fully evolved manner. Although Dandini's debt to Allori's painting technique and to Passignano's clear, strong colour is still in evidence, the influence of Mannerism—particularly of Bronzino—is seen in the saint's somewhat contrived pose.

Sir Francis Dashwood, Bt.

13 *St. Catherine of Alexandria*

Oil on canvas, (octagonal), 119.3 by 99 cms.

LITERATURE: McCorquodale, 1979(b).

St. Catherine lived in 3rd century Alexandria (see no. 45). Maximin II, who shared the Imperial crown with Constantine the Great and Licinius, chose Alexandria as his capital. Angry at St. Catherine's preaching and conversions, he ordered her execution by being torn to pieces by four spiked wheels. These were destroyed by heavenly flames, and so the saint was beheaded. The crown of flowers may refer to her royalty, while the palm is that of martyrdom and the book a symbol of her great learning.

A pair to no. 12, details such as the open book recalls Dandini's early experiments with Caravaggism (Borea, 1977). Although no date can be assigned to this picture, the handling of its drapery appears somewhat different from that in no. 12, and closer to that in the Vallombrosa *Conversion of St. Paul* and *Justice* (Munich, Private Collection: Kultzen, 1977, fig. 6).

Sir Francis Dashwood, Bt.

PIETRO DANDINI

Baldinucci mentions Pietro only in passing. He studied with his uncle, Vincenzo Dandini (1607-75), the brother of Cesare, whose version of the Roman classicism of Romanelli and Camassei certainly influenced Pietro's style, and to some extent his choice of themes. Dandini travelled to Rome, and also went to Venice, Emilia and Lombardy, and on his return to Florence obtained many important commissions, notably from the Grand Ducal family. For Vittoria della Rovere he worked at Poggio Imperiale and the Pitti, and for Cosimo III he painted frescoes at the Villa Petraia. Dandini was not always at his best in paintings with many figures, as is shown by his vacuous fresco of *Jerusalem stormed by the Pisans* in the Palazzo Comunale, Pisa; as his contemporaries noted, he excelled at painting rich costume, precious jewels and metalwork.

14 *An Allegory of Painting*

Oil on canvas, 68.5 by 60.3 cms.

LITERATURE: McCorquodale, 1979(b).

Formerly attributed to Gabbiani, this painting is highly characteristic of Dandini at his most refined. The harmonies of olive, pink, grey and blue and the general atmosphere of *deshabille* anticipate the Rococo, as does the free handling of paint and the lively turn of the head. Typical of Dandini are the large, soft eyes and small mouth, set in a face of great delicacy, and the influence of Pietro da Cortona's facial types is also evident. Similar female heads also appear in Dandini's *Miracle of the Blessed Giovacchino Piccolomini* of 1677 (Florence, SS. Annunziata) and *The Virgin in Glory* (Florence, S. Verdiana).

Private Collection.

Dolci was the most important native painter of the 17th century in Florence after Cristofano Allori, and established an international reputation in his own lifetime: this reputation was particularly strong in England, which until this century still held the largest number of his masterpieces. A child prodigy, he was trained under Jacopo Vignali, the melancholic religiosity of whose paintings in the later 1620's exercised profound influence on him. At fifteen, Dolci painted the portrait of *Stefano della Bella* and in the following year the remarkable *Fra' Ainolfo de' Bardi* (both Florence, Pitti Palace). Throughout his life he continued to paint superb portraits, and in this capacity was chosen to travel to Innsbruck in 1675 instead of the aged Sustermans to paint Claudia Felice de' Medici: this was the artist's sole long journey from Florence.

According to Baldinucci, Dolci manifested the intense religiosity which was the guiding force behind his art even as a child: this became increasingly obsessive, and Dolci conceived many of his works as of a votive nature, inscribing them with prayers (see No. 16) and aiming "to inspire Christian piety in those who beheld them" (Baldinucci). His two major paintings of the 1640's (Nos. 15, 25) show his superb technique already well-developed, and also his progress from a naturalism based on Rosselli, Vignali and Lippi towards his personal idealism, which, while never classical, is much more refined than the work of his contemporaries. Although he did paint a number of large altar-pieces such as *The Miracle at Soriano* of 1656 for S. Andrea a Cennano, Montevarchi (destroyed) and *The Vision of St. Louis of Toulouse* (Pitti), Dolci's ideal was increasingly realised in paintings with a single figure which confronts the spectator with striking simplicity and meticulous detail (see No. 17). In this he was probably influenced by Dutch paintings in the Medici collections, and was paralleled in Spain by Morales. Dolci's play on the sentiments and his ability to render mystical events arrestingly tangible relate him to other artists of the Baroque age like Bernini, and he exercised considerable—and often baneful—influence in this respect on later artists such as Greuze and even Tiepolo. He was also a still-life painter of some stature.

His painfully slow methods prevented him from working personally on the many commissions resulting from his great popularity and he was assisted by his daughter Agnese (d.1689) who, with Onorio Marinari (1627-1715?) succeeded in closely imitating certain aspects of his style. Other pupils like Bartolomeo Mancini merely initiated the oleographic tradition emanating from his work.

15 *Christ in the House of the Pharisee*

Oil on canvas, 170 by 216.5cms. Inscribed on the lower left corner of the socle of Christ's couch: "MDCIL AETATIS XXXIII CAROLUS DOLCIUS FLORENTINUS."

PROVENANCE: Antonio Lorenzo, Florence; Francis Colman; Sir Paul Methuen

LITERATURE: Baldinucci, 1846, IV, p. 637; Baldinucci, 1847, V, pp. 344-5; Gabburri, 1739, II, p. 524; Cambiagi, 1769–75, XI, p. 34, note 1; London and its Environs, 1761, III, p. 91 sq.; Martyn, 1766, II, p. 27; Britton, 1806, No. 53; Spiker, 1816, II, 127; Waagen, 1838, III, p. 101; Waagen, 1857 (Supplement), IV, p. 395; Borenius, 1939, No. 28; Del Bravo, 1963, p. 35, repr. fig. 42b; Kultzen, 1965, p. 186, note 17; McCorquodale, 1973, p. 482, and note 26, repr. fig. 5; Cantelli, 1977, p. 527; Thiem, 1977(b), p. 410, No. 220; McCorquodale, 1979(a)

EXHIBITED: British Institution, 1857, No. 123; Royal Academy, Winter Exhibition, 1950-51 No. 122

The theme is taken from Luke VII, 36-50. An unnamed prostitute, later traditionally identified with St. Mary Magdalen knowing that Christ was eating in the house of Simon the Pharisee, entered with an alabaster box of precious ointment with which she anointed Christ's feet after bathing them in her tears and drying them with her hair. Christ pointed to the Magdalen, saying that she was performing the customary courtesies which the Pharisee had failed to offer his guest, and that because of her humility her sins would be forgiven her.

Baldinucci recounts how Dolci, having for a long time admired Cornelius Galle's engraving after Lodovico Cigoli's *Christ in the House of the Pharisee*, resolved to paint a large version of it from the engraving. This he did, "studying every detail from nature", and the finished picture, having acquired considerable fame, was bought by the artist's physician, Antonio Lorenzi for one hundred and seventy *scudi*: the Marchese Filippo Niccolini was prepared to offer up to one thousand two hundred *scudi* for it but Lorenzi—to his subsequent regret—refused to part with the painting. In his life of Furini, Baldinucci says that Furini painted *The Marriage of the Virgin* for Lorenzi as a *pendant* to Dolci's "*tanto rinomato quadro della Maddalena in casa il (sic) Fariseo*". Since Furini died in 1646, this seems somewhat difficult to accept, but there is a remote possibility that the version of the picture formerly in the Leslie Collection was painted earlier than No. 14 and before Furini's death. Giuseppe Cantelli has recently proposed (Cantelli, 1977) that Furini's *Marriage of the Virgin* in the Bigongiari Collection, Florence was completed after Furini's death by Cecco Bravo and Simone Pignoni: this painting's dimensions are close to those of No. 15, and its composition suggests affinities with Dolci's picture. The whole problem is summarised in McCorquodale, 1979 (a).

Cigoli's picture was painted in 1596 for the noted classicist Girolamo Mercuriale, whose treatise *Gymnasium* discusses the Roman use of a *triclinium* (three couches around a dining table) such as appears in both the Cigoli (Blunt 1938-9) and the Dolci. Dolci's awareness of such archaeological accuracies is evidenced by his signature on the painting in imitation of incised Roman lettering. Significantly, Dolci used fewer figures than Cigoli in his composition, and heightened its drama by strong chiaroscuro, drawing more attention to the Magdalen. He also introduced a patently Tuscan collonade in the background, opulent colour and highly individual portraits in each of the heads. A preparatory study for the standing male servant at the right is in the Pushkin Museum, Moscow (Thiem, 1977, No. 220, repr. fig. 220) and a study of Christ's profile was sold at Christie's, 30th March 1976, lot 40 (McCorquodale, 1979 (a)). Del Bravo published an associated oil study in the National Museum, Stockholm (op. cit. 1963, fig. 42a).

Lent from the Methuen Collection.

16   *The Guardian Angel*

Oil on panel 43 by 33cms. Inscribed on the back of the panel, in Dolci's hand: "*Opera di Carlin' Dolci*" followed by a Latin inscription relating to the picture's theme.

PROVENANCE: Alessandro Valori, Florence (?); Sir Paul Methuen, and by descent to the present Lord Methuen.

LITERATURE: Baldinucci, 1847, V, p. 347; London and its Environs, 1761, III, p. 87; Martyn, 1766, II, p. 20; Britton, 1806, No. 11; Waagen, 1838, III, p. 105; Waagen, 1857 (Supplement), IV. p. 397; Corsham Catalogue, 1891, No. 210; Corsham Catalogue, 1903, No. 143; McCorquodale, 1976, pp. 315-16, fig. 2.

EXHIBITED: British Institution, 1857, No. 19; Burlington Fine Arts Club, Exhibition of Italian Art of the 17th Century, 1925, No. 7

There seems little doubt that this is the picture described by Baldinucci as having been painted by Dolci for Alessandro Valori: "a small picture (*quadretto*), in which is represented the Guardian Angel, in the act of showing the way to Heaven to the Christian soul, represented by a graceful little girl in a white dress."

This and *The Flight into Egypt* (No. 19) probably date from around 1650, when Dolci was experimenting with a lyrical, soft-outline style in small-scale pictures (McCorquodale, op. cit.): a small panel of *The Penitent St. Jerome* in a similar style and dated 1647 was recently on the London art market, and showed the same interest in atmospheric landscape detail. Dolci may have evolved this type of picture—so different in style from his larger, more finished compositions—from the backgrounds in such works as *St. Andrew adoring his Cross* (No. 25) where such small figures proliferate.

Lent from the Methuen Collection.

17 *Christ consecrating the Elements*

Oil on canvas, 87.5 by 72.3cms. Inscribed on the back of the stretcher, "*1608 il primo di Luglio Ottaua del Glorioso Santo Giovanni Batista principia . . . (further words illegible.)*"

PROVENANCE: Sir Paul Methuen (1672-1757) and by descent to the present Lord Methuen

LITERATURE: Baldinucci, 1847, V. p. 356; London and its Environs, 1761, III, p. 97; Martyn, 1766, II, p. 97; Britton, 1806, No. 134; Spiker, 1816, II, p. 129; Waagen, 1838, III, p. 96; Waagen, 1857 (Supplement), IV, p. 395; Corsham Catalogue 1891, No. 207; Corsham Catalogue, 1903, No. 199; Borenius, 1939, No. 29; McCorquodale, 1976, p. 316

ENGRAVED: By Earlom for Boydell, 1769

EXHIBITED: British Institution, 1857, No. 56; Burlington House, 1938, No. 292 (as *Salvator Mundi*)

Baldinucci (op. cit.) noted that "*Del Cristo son fuori più originali: siccome di una mezza figura del medesimo, in atto di benedire il pane.*" Chronologically, this occurs in Baldinucci's account shortly before Luca Giordano's arrival in Florence (1682) and at the same time as Dolci painted his *Charity* (McCorquodale, 1973, p. 482 and fig. 13) dateable to 1675-80: there is therefore little doubt that this painting is one of the "several originals" to which Baldinucci refers. Two other versions (Burghley House, Marquess of Exeter Collection, and Dresden, Gemäldegalerie) are certainly autograph works and in 1677 another was recorded in Pistoia Cathedral (Busse, 1913).

In this and similar paintings of the later 1670's and early 1680's, Dolci seems to have realized his own ideal of devotional imagery (Heintz, 1960). By means of rigorously simplified composition, preferably with a single figure filling the entire picture, Dolci achieved a degree of intense concentration on the painting's theme rare in seventeenth century art. Using the highest possible degree of surface realism (which led Ruskin to describe Dolci's pictures as "polished into inanity") Dolci gave every detail of such paintings equal prominence with the result that both figures and still-life have a disturbing "presence". Details such as the light reflected from the paten onto the underside of Christ's hand, the minutely-observed linen and the curls of His hair all contribute to this somewhat hallucinatory quality.

Dolci appears to have used a study in the British Museum for the right arm and hand of his *Charity* in slightly modified form for that of Christ in this picture (McCorquodale, op. cit., p. 320, repr. fig. 7).

It does not appear to have been noted that John Constable derived his *Christ blessing the Sacraments* of 1810 (Nayland, St. James's Church) from this picture by Dolci.

Lent from the Methuen Collection.

18 *St. Ursula*

Oil on panel (circular), diameter, including frame, 45.2cm.

PROVENANCE: William Kent; Nathaniel Curzon, later 1st Lord Scarsdale
LITERATURE: Waagen, 1838, III, p. 393 (as St. Ursula)

The origin of the story of St. Ursula is Geoffrey de Monmouth's *Historia Regum Britanniae*. Ursula, daughter of an English King was betrothed to a pagan king, whom she insisted on taking to Rome to convert. She took with her ten young noblewomen, one of whom may have been called Undicimilla (Italian = eleven thousand): through a later misreading of a manuscript, this may have been interpreted as the number of Ursula's virgin followers who were massacred with her outside Cologne on their return from Rome. Ursula herself was shot with arrows, and is the patroness of the Ursulines.

An inscription on the back of the panel describes No. 18 as St. Christiana, an extremely obscure saint, and it is more likely on account of her gold crown and the arrow that the saint is St. Ursula. The picture surface and its frame are carved from a single piece of wood, the frame deliberately evoking perhaps those on marble or ceramic *tondi* of the Quattrocento.

The picture was purchased by Nathaniel Curzon, later 4th Baronet and 1st Lord Scarsdale, at his agent Mr. Kent's sale in February 1758, and probably hung in his London house until *circa* 1773 when it was taken to Kedleston (information kindly supplied by Mr. Leslie Harris).

Viscount Scarsdale, Kedleston Hall, Derbyshire.

19   *The Flight into Egypt*

Oil on canvas, 36.2 by 49 cms.

PROVENANCE: Andrea del Rosso, Florence; 5th Marquess of Exeter.
LITERATURE: Baldinucci, 1846, V. p. 347; Burghley Guide, 1815, p. 17; Waterhouse, 1960,
              p. 54f, fig. 5; Haskell, 1963, p. 211; McCorquodale, 1976, p. 315; Thiem, 1977
              (b), pp. 407-10, fig. 306
EXHIBITED: Royal Academy, 1960, *Italian Art and Britain*, No. 24

The theme is taken from Matthew, 2: 13-23. St. Joseph, warned by an angel of Herod's impending Massacre of the Innocents, fled with the Virgin and Child from Bethlehem to Egypt, where the Holy Family remained for two years. Dolci shows the continuing journey of the Holy Family after the Rest on the Flight (see No. 53), since the Child carries the roses which supposedly sprang up wherever the Family stopped, and they are being guided by one of the angels who ministered to them during the Rest.

Two paintings of this theme were in the collection of Andrea del Rosso, one of which he sent to the Marquess of Exeter in England (Baldinucci, op. cit.). No. 19 is this picture, but cannot have been painted by Dolci for del Rosso (who was born only in 1640), presumably entering his collection later. The second version of the theme belonging to del Rosso may be identical with that recorded in the Ginori collection in Florence in 1724 (Borroni-Salvadori, 1974, p. 80) and with Victor Spark, New York, in 1966. A dating in the later 1640's suggested by stylistic similarities with *The Guardian Angel* (No. 16) (McCorquodale, op. cit.) seems to be confirmed by the similarity of the preparatory study for the angel (Rome, Gabinetto Nazionale delle Stampe) with other studies for dated paintings of the 1640's (Thiem, op. cit.).

Imbued with a charming freshness, this and No. 16 exemplify the poetic naturalism of Dolci's art before the gradual intensification during the 1650's of his pietistic imagery. The narrative simplicity of the scene recalls some of Vignali's smaller paintings, but the soft outlines, delicate gestures and sweet facial expressions are wholly Dolci's.

The Marquess of Exeter

20 *Madonna and Child*

Oil on copper, 19 by 13.3cm.

LITERATURE: Gambiagi, 1769-75, XI, p. 40, note 2; Waagen, 1854, II, p. 151; McCorquodale, 1973, p. 488, note 10, and repr. fig. 18; McCorquodale, 1976, p. 317 and note 25

EXHIBITED: British Institution, 1843, No. 73; 1865, No. 42.

ENGRAVED: By Francesco Bartolozzi (as an oval)

Baldinucci (1847, V. pp. 346-7) noted Dolci's talent (*bel genio*) for painting small figures, in which he had a unique style which fetched high prices. Gambiagi (op. cit.) noted "Two tiny images of Mary painted . . . on copper, one a *tondo* of the sorrowing Virgin, the other suckling the Holy Child, both to be found in London, where they have been engraved by the famous Florentine engraver Francesco Bartolozzi: these precious prints well convey the perfection and beauty of their originals." (Waagen op. cit.) described No. 20 as "less affected in character than is often the case in his pictures."

The iconography of the Madonna suckling the Child is not common in Italian painting, and while this picture recalls the Leonardo school *Madonna Litta* (Leningrad, Hermitage) a more likely source seems to lie in the works of Northern painters. Certainly, the glimpsed landscape appears to be of Northern derivation. Its naturalism and charming freshness must have appealed to eighteenth century English taste, especially as reproduced through the medium of Bartolozzi's engraving.

Lent by kind permission of the Trustees of the Bowood Settlement

21 *Sir Thomas Baines*

Oil on canvas, 86.4 by 71.1cm. Inscribed, on table covering: *Sir Thos Baines*

PROVENANCE: Finch Family, Burley-on-the-Hill; Major James Hanbury; Sir Thomas Barlow; S. V. Christie-Millar, Esq.

LITERATURE: Baldinucci, 1847, V. p. 352; Cust and Malloch, 1916, pp. 292-7; Haskell, 1963, p. 197; Del Bravo, 1963, p. 37, and fig. 49; McCorquodale, 1973, p. 481, and fig. 8; McCorquodale, 1976, p. 313, p. 315

EXHIBITED: London, Magnasco Society, 1924, No. 26; London, Royal Academy, Winter Exhibition 1930, No. 484; London, Royal Academy, 1950, "*Works by Holbein and other Masters of the 16th and 17th Centuries*", No. 299; London, Royal Academy, 1960, "*Italian Art and Britain*", No. 10

Sir Thomas Baines (1622-80) was educated at Christ College, Cambridge, where he met his lifelong companion, Sir John Finch (1626-1682). He accompanied Finch to Italy and was created doctor of physic at Padua, receiving the same degree on his return to Cambridge in 1660. With Finch during his period as English Resident at the court of the Grand Duke Ferdinand II in 1665-70, when he probably met Dolci (McCorquodale, 1976), he later went with his friend to Constantinople where they were known as "the Ambassador and the chevalier". His prolonged absence lost him his chair at Cambridge, and he died at Constantinople. Finch had his body embalmed and returned with it to Cambridge in 1682, when both were buried in the same grave.

Baldinucci (op. cit.) refers to Finch's collecting (see No. 24) and to a portrait of him (Cambridge, Fitzwilliam Museum) and that of "dottor Fava, suo confidentissimo gentiluomo". Fava, Italian for beans (ie beans = Baines), was presumably only Baldinucci's Italianisation of the name, although some play on words may have been intended.

Painted by Dolci together with its pair, *Sir John Finch* between 1665-70, and probably sent back to England with the other paintings which Finch had bought from Dolci (McCorquodale, 1976), two of which he gave to the Royal Family (see No. 23) the *Baines* seems to have formed the centrepiece of the first important collection of Dolci's painting in England. During 1681, Finch sent a further four Dolci paintings to his family (McCorquodale, 1976): unfortunately the whole collection was dispersed in 1947.

Curiously, No. 21 is of infinitely higher quality than the Finch portrait, and in its evocation of the refined, scholarly world of the sitter places it among the portrait masterpieces of the 17th century. Appropriately, as a former pupil of the noted Cambridge Platonist Henry More, Baines pauses in his reading of Plato (symbolically resting on Aristotle) and is surrounded by the works of other classical writers including Euclid and Hippocrates. So different from Dolci's earlier portraits, its sober objectivity and psychological acuity seem more Dutch than Italian, and prefigure major portraits of the 1670's like those of the Archduchess Claudia de' Medici.

The Fitzwilliam Museum, Cambridge.

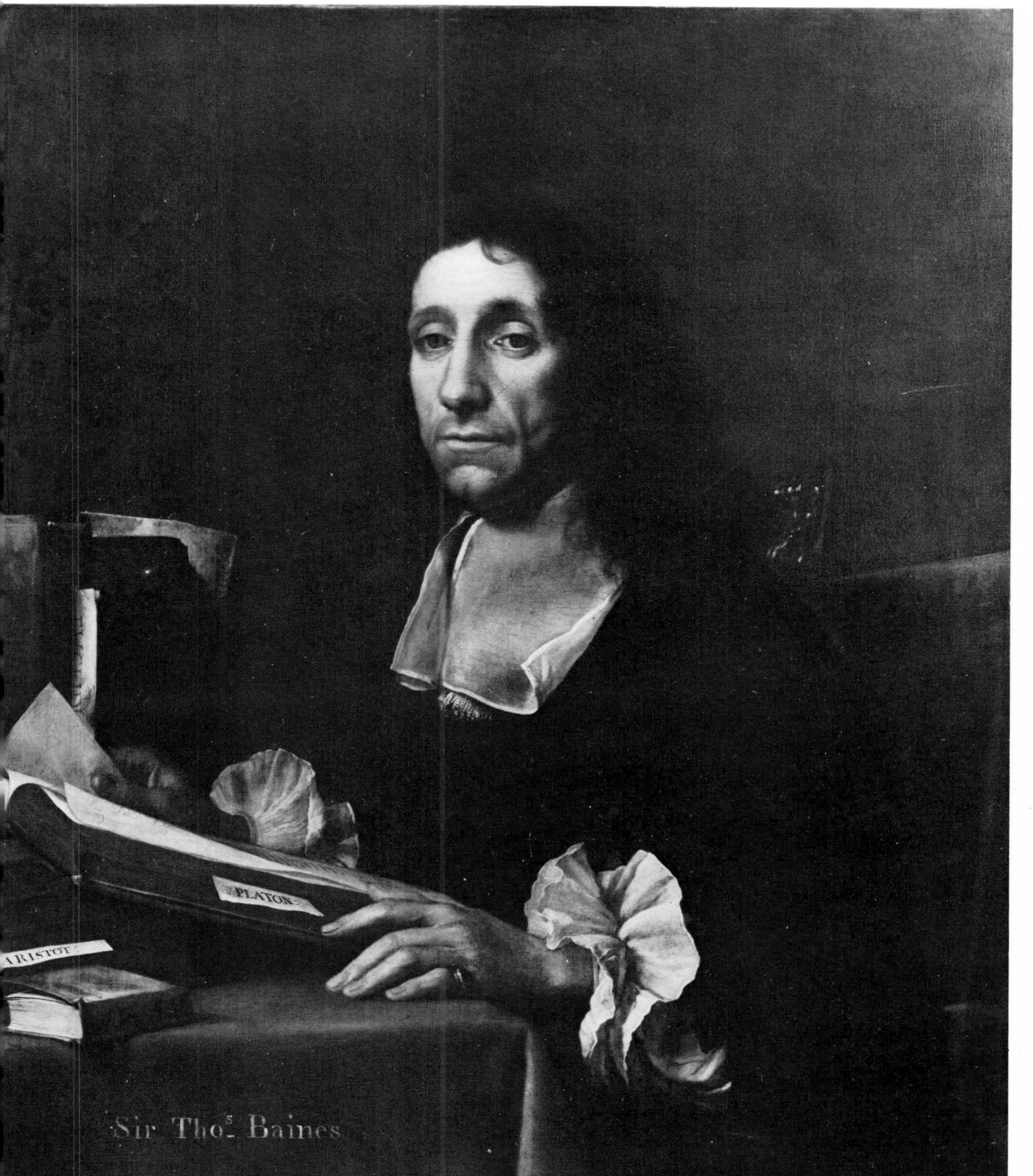
PLATON
ARISTOT
Sir Thos. Baines

22   *Hagar and the Angel*

Oil on canvas, 91.5 by 123.8 cms. Signed below water vase: Carlo Dolci

PROVENANCE: Exeter Collection(?), Lord Wenlock, and by descent to N. Forbes Adam.
LITERATURE: Gambiagi, 1769-75, XI, p. 37; McCorquodale, 1979
EXHIBITED: British Institution, 1853, No. 95; Leeds, 1868, No. 125

For the story of Hagar, see No. 55.

Baldinucci states that Andrea del Rosso (see No. 19) owned *The Story of Hagar and Ishmael* *"in figure maggiore di braccio"*, mentioning it coincidentally with other paintings all dating from before 1650. Gambiagi (op. cit.) also noted the del Rosso painting, but added that "The same story, with a different composition, was painted by Carlo for a certain Lord Exeter, who sent it to England". The del Rosso family exhibited their version in Florence in 1724 and again in 1767 (Borroni-Salvadori, 1974, pp. 80-81). It seems likely that No. 22 is the version painted for Lord Exeter.

The pose of Hagar seems to have been borrowed from Furini's rendering of the theme (Florence, Bigongiari Collection: Bigongiari, 1971): this may explain the somewhat more "Baroque" treatment of the figure than is usual with Dolci, since Furini appears to have responded strongly to Cortona's Florentine style. Another source may lie in Cigoli's version in reverse (Frascati, Villa Muti). Striking too is the inclusion of such a large area of landscape—to which the figures are not entirely satisfactorily related—handled with considerable atmosphere, and similar to those in the background of No. 22.

Private Collection

23 *Salome with the Head of St. John the Baptist*

Oil on canvas, 119.5 by 95 cms.

PROVENANCE: Henry Hoare, Stourhead, before 1785; Stourhead Heirlooms Sale, Christie's, 2 June 1883, lot 65 bought for Glasgow Art Gallery through Sir Charles Robinson

LITERATURE: Del Bravo, 1963, p. 37 and fig 47; Levey, 1964, p. 76, No. 464; Ewald, 1974, No. 124; McCorquodale, 1976, p. 320; McCorquodale, 1977, pp. 55-9, and fig. 2

EXHIBITED: London, Royal Academy, 1930, No. 753. London, Royal Academy, 1962, *Primitives to Picasso*, No. 102

In Matthew XIV, 6-11, the unnamed daughter of Herodias and step-daughter of Herod Antipas danced for Herod on his birthday, and on being promised whatever she wanted, asked for the head of John the Baptist in a charger. When this was brought to her, she carried it to her mother. The name of Salome was only connected with the story later, and was often confused with that of Herodias, who was traditionally in love with the Baptist as Herod was with her daughter. There is little doubt, in view of the model's age and the fact that she carries the head on a charger that No. 22 shows Salome and not Herodias as Baldinucci states.

Baldinucci says that Dolci's *Herodiad*, painted for the Marchese Rinuccini, was his most popular work. The vexed question of the identity of the original canvas, which hung until 1870 in the company of its pendant *David with the Head of Goliath* (No. 24) until 1870, hinges on the description and engraving in the San Donato Sale Catalogue (McCorquodale, 1977). Like the *David*, the original *Salome* bore a stretcher inscription, recording the first payment to the artist in November, 1678. From the engraving in the San Donato Catalogue, it is clear that the Salome in the Rinuccini original wore no bracelets, whereas, with the exception of the Dresden version (whose provenance starts in Paris in the 18th century) all the other known versions of any quality have bracelets. Baldinucci noted three versions, saying that the *second* was for Sir John Finch (see No. 21) and that he gave it to King Charles II (Hampton Court, H.M. The Queen: Levey, 1964). No. 23 is the finest known version apart from that in Dresden: another good version was in the Segrè-Sartorio Collection in Trieste. Studio copies are in the Victoria and Albert Museum, Phoenix Art Museum, Boston Museum of Fine Arts and Palazzo Madama, Rome (on loan from the Florentine Galleries): further versions have passed through the salerooms.

The Royal Collection version is therefore the only one securely documented as Dolci's. In contrast to the grisly heroines of Furini and Ficherelli, this *Salome* has an innocent purity totally at variance with the theme.

Glasgow Art Gallery

24 *David with the Head of Goliath*

Oil on canvas, 131.5 by 104 cms. Inscribed on rock: 1680 FCD FLOR

PROVENANCE: Marchese Pier Francesco Rinuccini, Florence; Prince Anton Demidoff, Florence

LITERATURE: Baldinucci, 1847, V, pp. 351-2; Gambiagi, 1769-75, XI, p. 35; Fantozzi, 1842, p. 728; Rinuccini, 1852, lot 254; Dandolo, 1863, p. 196; San Donato, 1870, p. 110, No. 149; McCorquodale, 1977, pp. 55-59, repr. pl. 1 and cover (colour)

1 Samuel XVII, 12-51 recounts how the giant, Goliath came forward from the ranks of the Philistines, with whom Saul and the Israelites were about to do battle, and challenged them all. David, a youthful Israelite who had been sent with provisions to the battlefront by chance, slew the giant with a slung stone and decapitated him with his own huge sword.

One of the masterpieces of the Florentine seventeeth century, Dolci's *David* was painted as the pair to his *Salome* for the Marchese Pier Francesco Rinuccini (see No. 23), and hung with the *Salome* until 1870 (McCorquodale, op. cit. p. 55 and note 3). The *David* is an especially important document of Dolci's notoriously slow working methods, since on the painting's stretcher are inscribed details in Dolci's hand of each payment received from the Marchese as work progressed (repr. McCorquodale, op. cit. pl. 3). According to these inscriptions, and documents in the Rinuccini archives (San Donato, op. cit.) Dolci started work on the painting on the 10th July, 1670 (ie 1669) and received his final payment on 8th March 1681 (1680). A preparatory drawing for the entire figure in Bucharest (Thiem 1977 (b), p. 409, repr. pl. 308) is inscribed in a hand other than the artist's (in Italian): "Sketch (pensiero) by Carlin Dolci for the David. Painted for the Most Illustrious Signore Marchese Folco Rinuccini in 1679." Thiem associates the drawing with the version in the Brera, which is signed and dated 1670, and was probably the version recorded by Baldinucci as having been painted for the British Resident at the Medici Court, Sir John Finch (McCorquodale, 1976, pp. 313-5, and op. cit. pp. 56-7).

P. & D. Colnaghi and Co.

25 *St. Andrew adoring His Cross*

Oil on canvas, 111.5 by 91.5cm. Signed, bottom right '*Carolus Dolcius Florentinus Fact. 1643.*

PROVENANCE: Paolo del Sera, Florence/Venice; Sir James Colebrooke, Bt. of Gatton; Sold, Prestage and Hobbs, London, 4.2.1762, Lot 70; Thomas Duncombe, by descent to the Earls of Feversham; Agnew's, 1962

LITERATURE: Baldinucci, 1847, V. p. 347; Gambiagi, 1769-75, XI, p. 37; Fry, 1926, pp. 111 and 225, Pl. XXIII; Woodward, 1963, p. 250, repr. (colour) fig. VI; del Bravo, 1963, p. 34; O. Sitwell, 1964, p. 383, fig. V; del Bravo, 1967(b), p. 223; McCorquodale, 1973, p. 482, repro. fig. 6; Chiarini, 1978 (a), pp. 90-91; McCorquodale, 1979 (a).

EXHIBITED: British Institution, 1855, No. 21; Leeds, 1868, No. 157; Agnew's, *Magnasco Society Exhibition*, 1925 (24); Wildenstein, 1970, Cat. No. 16, figs. 16, 16a

ENGRAVED: By Carlo Faucci, 1759, 1768

St. Andrew, brother of Simon Peter, was the first Apostle. He is only mentioned by name in the Gospels subsequently, but legend has it that after the Ascension he travelled to Scythia, Cappadocia and Bithynia, effecting many conversions. Angry at his prosylitizing in Patras, the proconsul Aegeus had him crucified. His cross (*crux decussata* or saltire) was of a different form from that of Christ, and he is reputed to have fallen on his knees and adored it because on it he was to die in the same way as Christ: he was however tied, not nailed to it.

According to Baldinucci, Dolci painted the first of three versions of this theme for the Florentine Senator Paolo del Sera, who later took the picture to Venice, where it established Dolci's fame in that city. Two other versions listed by Baldinucci "with the same composition, although of different sizes" were painted for the Marchese Carlo Gerini (now Florence, Pitti: Ewald, 1976) and for Carlo Corbinelli (Chiarini, op. cit. and McCorquodale, 1979 (a)). No. 25 is listed in the inventory of del Sera's collection made at Venice on 11th July 1674, and according to Gambiagi (op. cit.) was "purchased by an English gentleman, who, before taking to to London, had it engraved by the excellent Florentine engraver Carlo Faucci for the price of 100 sequins." This picture is a rich document both of Dolci's art and of contemporary Florentine collecting and patronage, the full range of whose sources and references remains to be completely investigated (McCorquodale, 1979(a)). Not only does the painting contain portraits of some of Dolci's leading Florentine contemporaries, but also—among the background crowd— quotations from paintings which may have been in the del Sera collection. Baldinucci unfortunately identifies only one figure, that of the armed man with a moustache, whom he says is Raffaello Ximines (a noted connoisseur and one of Dolci's earliest patrons). Each of the other foreground figures is clearly a portrait too, and Dolci himself appears as the tiny figure beneath the saint's right hand. Between the legs of the youth supporting the cross are tiny copies of Titian's *Youth with a Fur Collar* (New York, Frick Collection) of which Dolci made a drawing (Del Bravo, 1967(b)) and an oriental possibly from a Rubens *Adoration* at Lyons (Jaffé, 1977). The head of the bearded man inclined away from the latter two is borrowed from one of Cristofano Allori's studies of St. Julian, of which Colci also made an oval copy (McCorquodale, 1979(a)). The Pitti version is dated 1646 and varies considerably in detail from No. 24.

The theme of St. Andrew's martyrdom appears to have enjoyed a sudden vogue during the first half of the 17th century in Florentine painting, the most notable examples being by Rosselli (c. 1620, Florence, Ognissanti) and Lippi's of 1639 now in Sant'Agata. Although Dolci borrowed from each of these, he transcended his prototypes by his addition of sparkling colour, rich detail and highly romantic landscape which recalls Andrea del Sarto's Borgherini panels.

A study for the youth supporting the cross is in the Ashmolean Museum, Oxford (Parker, 1956) and appears to show the same model used by Dolci for the servant in his *Christ in the House of the Pharisee* (No. 15).

Birmingham City Museum and Art Gallery

FELICE FICHERELLI, *called* IL RIPOSO *c.* 1605 San Gimignano-1669 Florence

Ficherelli, who was nicknamed *Il Riposo* because of his retiring nature, was brought to Florence as a boy by Count Alberto de' Bardi, where he entered the studio of Jacopo da Empoli. Empoli's narrative directness remained the principal influence in Ficherelli's art, and he inherited Empoli's talent as a copyist of earlier masters such as Perugino, whose *Vision of St. Bernard* (Munich, Alte Pinakothek) from S. Spirito he replaced with an indistinguishable copy. He registered with the Accademia del Disegno in 1629, and came under the influence of Biliverti and Furini during the 1630's, when he probably first took an interest in the morbid, ambiguous themes which distinguish many of his paintings. To Empoli's luminous handling of paint, Ficherelli added his own interest in rich texture and colour. In his large commissions such as *The Virgin and Child with Saints* of 1654-7 (Florence, S. Maria Nuova) or the damaged *St. Philip Neri* of 1657 (Florence, Certosa) he adopts a style closely based on Empoli, and his most original contribution lies in private commissions on a smaller scale: their subjects are often chosen for the conflicting sentiments which they arouse, usually a mixture in varying degrees of revulsion with perverse fascination, pity with prurience. Examples are *Julia receiving the Bloodstained Garments of Pompey* (Genoa, Michetti Collection), *Tarquin and Lucretia* (Rome, Accademia di San Luca) and *St. Praxedis collecting the Blood of the Martyrs* (Florence, del Bravo Collection) which appears to have been copied by Vermeer.

26 *Lot and His Daughters*

Oil on canvas, 159 by 176 cms.

PROVENANCE: Milltown Collection

LITERATURE: Neale, 1826, III.

After the destruction of Sodom and Gomorrah, Lot and his two daughters fled to the mountains and lived in a cave. The two girls, in order to ensure the preservation of their line, plied the old man with wine, and committed incest with him: their children were Moab and Ben-ammi.

This painting must be ranked among Ficherelli's more important works, and is similar in handling to *Tobias restoring his Father's Sight* in a Florentine Private Collection (Gregori, 1974, fig. 27): both have the same interest in heavy fabrics and share the dense paint structure with which Ficherelli characteristically creates an impression of solid, tangible form. Gregori dates the *Tobias* to *circa* 1650, and a similar dating seems acceptable for No. 26. Its technique is also similar to that of a *Magdalen* by Ficherelli in the Bigongiari Collection, Florence, which appears to be of the same period. Certain compositional analogies also exist with a painting of the same theme in the Palazzo Rospigliosi at Pistoia, attributed by Ewald to Lupicini (Ewald, 1965), whose technique may have influenced Ficherelli.

National Gallery of Ireland, Dublin

27 *Sophonisba about to drink the Poison*

Oil on canvas (oval), 72.5 by 52.5 cms.

LITERATURE: McCorquodale, 1979 (b).

The principal account of Sophonisba (or Sophoniba) is found in Livy's *History of Rome*, Book XXX, 12f. She was the wife of Syphax, King of Carthage. Scipio, aided by Massinissa, defeated Carthage, and Sophonisba, then "remarkably beautiful and in the full bloom of youth", and like all her race "excessively amorous" (Livy) pressed her favours on Massinissa. They were married but Massinissa was reproved by Scipio, and sent Sophonisba a cup of poison to ensure that she would not fall into Roman hands. She drank it, regretting only the disappointingly short time between her marriage and her death.

This is a particularly beautiful example of Ficherelli's use of a dark underpainting which gives the flesh a characteristic density, contrasting with the crisp folds of the white chemise. The parted lips, large appealing eyes and the garment's calculatedly negligent disarray revealing one shoulder and breast appear in several other works by Ficherelli such as his *Patience* (Florence, Bigongiari Collection: Gregori 1974, fig. 23) and *Lucretia* (Florence, Private Collection: Cantelli, 1977, fig. 497).

No. 27 was formerly attributed to Furini. George III acquired a painting of the same theme by Furini with the collection of Consul Smith (Levey, 1964, p. 80).

P. & D. Colnaghi & Co.

BALDASSARE FRANCESCHINI, *called* IL VOLTERRANO

1611 Volterra-1689 Florence

Volterrano is one of the most underestimated decorative painters of the Italian Baroque, but was also a fine portraitist. He entered Rosselli's studio at sixteen, and after briefly assisting Giovanni da San Giovanni with his frescoes in the *Sala terrena* of the Pitti Palace, escaped the latter's jealousy of his precocity and received a highly important personal commission from Don Lorenzo de' Medici. This was for the frescoes on two sides of the courtyard at the Villa Petraia. Volterrano worked there from 1636-46 with a break in 1641 during which Don Lorenzo sent him to Venice and Parma, to study Correggio's dome frescoes. Despite the advances which the Petraia frescoes made on Giovanni da San Giovanni's style, Cortona's Pitti decorations of 1637-47 made the latter's work appear outdated, and he modified it accordingly: nonetheless he had no other equal in Florence until the arrival of Luca Giordano in 1682. Don Lorenzo's death in 1648 robbed Volterrano of a valuable patron, but he continued to work for the Medici, at the Pitti, the Villa Poggio Imperiali and in various churches. His fully developed style, while much more suave than Giovanni da San Giovanni's, never became as wholly Baroque as Giordano's, although his palette also prefigures the 18th century with its pale blues, yellow and green. His major undertaking was the huge fresco of *Coronation of the Virgin* of 1681-3 in the tribune cupola of the SS. Annunziata, which cannot be judged a complete success and is difficult to see on account of poor lighting, but his decorations in the Niccolini Chapel in S. Croce, (1652-64) the *salone* of the Palazzo della Gherardesca and the Palazzo Duca di S. Clemente all show him at his best. His canvases depend on the style and feeling for scale of his frescoes, although he was capable of great delicacy of detail.

28 *Diana resting*

Oil on canvas, oval, 54 by 62 cms.

Diana, Goddess of the Moon and of the hunt, is seen resting, with one of her hounds. This is a variant of Volterrano's *Reading Magdalen* (Udine, Museo Civico: Ewald, 1973, fig. 9) and is very close in pose to his *Sleeping Cupid* (Burghley House, Marquess Exeter). It is also close in style to *Venus and Cupid* (Raleigh, Marshall Collection: Ewald, 1973, fig. 12). An amalgam of the influences of Giovanni da San Giovanni's informal approach to mythology with Furini's *sfumato*, a dating of 1635-8 may be tentatively suggested, after Volterrano's collaboration with Giovanni da San Giovanni in the Sala degli Argenti but before the impact of Cortona's frescoes in the Sala della Stufa. A comparison with Volterrano's *Hylas* (No. 29) shows that the *bravura* handling of the latter is already prefigured here in a restrained way which distinguishes it immediately from Furini's manner.

Captain P. J. B. Drury-Lowe, from the Locko Park Collection

29 *Hylas*

Oil on canvas, 100 by 85cm.

PROVENANCE: Jacopo del Turco, Florence (before 1681); Marchese Carlo Gerini

LITERATURE: Baldinucci, 1847, V. p. 177; Catalogo e stima dei quadri . . ., 1825, No. 227; Ewald, 1976, p. 345 and note 8, p. 356, repr. fig. 5.

EXHIBITED: London, Trafalgar Galleries, *In the Light of Caravaggio*, 1976, No. 17, repr. (colour).

Hylas, the handsome companion of Hercules, was a member of the expedition of the Argonauts: when their ship reached the coasts of the Troad, Hylas was sent to seek fresh water. The nymphs of the spring were so captivated by his beauty that they dragged him down to the water's depths, and he was never seen again. Hylas's fate is illustrated in the relief on his water vase, the central group of which bears some resemblance to the most famous rendering of the theme in the Florentine Seicento by Furini, now in the Pitti Palace.

Although not included among the other Volterrano pictures listed in the Gerini collection by Bocchi-Cinelli (1677) or the *Raccolta di ottanta stampe rappresentanti i quadri più scelti de'SSig. Marchesi Gerini* of 1786, this is certainly the picture described in the 1825 Gerini Catalogue (op. cit.) as a "*mezza figura al naturale*". Baldinucci (op. cit.) says that it passed from the collection of Jacopo del Turco to the Gerini, and the painting retains its Gerini frame.

Handled with a boldness which recalls Volterrano's technique in fresco painting, the generalised style of No. 29 suggests a dating close to his *The Way to Calvary* (Florence, Marchesi Gerini), painted for the Marchesi Carlo Gerini as a pendant to *The Flight into Egypt* which came from the collection of Cardinal Gian Carlo de' Medici (died 1663). The *Hylas* is painted with dark outlining of facial and other detail which distinguishes it from the softer manner of the *Rest on the Flight*, painted under the impact of Cortona's Florentine frescoes. This type of large-featured, androgynous beauty is however peculiar to Volterrano, and is very far removed from the disturbed—and disturbing—ambiguity of Hylas's expression in Furini's painting.

A small fresco oval of this theme by Volterrano is in the Museo Bardini, Florence, and Baldinucci records other versions of *Hylas* for Costimo Citerni and Francesco Parrocchiani.

Private Collection

FRANCESCO FURINI

Furini was the son of the painter Filippo Furini, known as Pippo Sciamerone, from whose studio he passed to those of Passignano, Biliverti and lastly, Rosselli. He was one of the most influential painters of his period in Florence. In Rome from 1619-22, where he studied briefly with Bartolomeo Manfredi, he worked on the frescoes in Palazzo Bentivoglio with Giovanni da San Giovanni, with whom he had studied under Rosselli. Returning to Florence, he registered at the Accademia del Disegno in 1625. In 1629, he went to Venice to paint a companion piece to a picture by Reni, and in 1633 became the priest of Sant'Ansano in the Mugello.

Already in his earliest known painting, *Cephalus and Aurora* of 1623-4 (Ponce, Art Museum), Furini showed an interest in soft, fleshy forms and romantic atmosphere, which he further evolved by means of delicate *sfumato* effects and the study of Guido Reni's female nudes. According to Baldinucci, Furini incurred repeated debts through his use of the most beautiful (and expensive) female models, and Lanzi commented (1795-6) that his cabinet-paintings were "for the most part, Nymphs, and also Magdalens who wear little more than the Nymphs . . ." The ambiguous *Hylas and the Nymphs* of 1630 (Florence, Pitti) is the apotheosis of this most important aspect of his output, from which his pupil Pignoni derived much of his inspiration. After Giovanni da San Giovanni's death in 1636, Furini participated with Ottavio Vannini and Cecco Bravo in the completion of the frescoes in the Sala terrena (now Museo degli Argenti) of Palazzo Pitti, contributing *Lorenzo the Magnificent with his artists* and *The Death of Lorenzo*.

Furini's crisis of conscience and temporary assumption of the priesthood during which time he painted only religious themes, must have had repercussions among other Florentine artists, but did not prevent Pignoni from developing even more voluptuous versions of Furini's style after his death.

30 *Sigismunda with the Heart of Guiscardo*

Oil on canvas, 73 by 59 cms.

PROVENANCE: Sir Luke Schaub; Sir Thomas Sebright; Earl of Lincoln

LITERATURE: Bürger, 1857, p. 108; Waagen, 1857 (Supplement), p. 510; Wind, 1938-9; Antal, 1947, fig. 19; Saxl-Wittkower, 1948, No. 61, fig. a; Tomory, 1972, pp. 94-5; Gould 1976, p. 289

EXHIBITED: Manchester, 1857, Art Treasures Exhibition, No. 348; Nottingham Castle, 1879

ENGRAVED: By J. McArdell (as Correggio, when in Schaub collection)

The story of Sigismunda (or Ghismonda) is told Boccaccio's *Decameron*, IV, 1. She was the only child of Tancred, Prince of Salerno, in deference to whom she had taken a lover—the handsome servant Guiscardo—rather than remarry after the premature death of her husband the Duke of Capua. Observed by Tancred *in flagrante delicto*, Sigismunda refused to renounce her low-born lover and Tancred had him strangled, sending his daughter Guiscardo's heart in a gold cup. Sigismunda wept copiously over the heart, added poison to the cup, and drank the mixture. As she lay dying, she passionately kissed the heart and clasped it to her bosom.

Sigismunda is the most lugubrious of Furini's paintings, combining a sinister eroticism with particularly gruesome necrophilia. Typical of Furini are the heavy eyelids and full, small mouth with its curving upper lip; these features occur in the face of Hylas in *Hylas and the Nymphs*, to which No. 30 is close in style and in its heavy chiaroscuro. A variant with an urn, described as a *Magdalen* is in the Gemäldegalerie, Vienna: there seems no reason to suppose that it does not represent *Sigismunda* also. Furini used the same pose, in reverse, in his *Poetry* formerly in the Cremer Collection, (Toesca, 1950, pl. 43), and the pose reappears in several other Florentine half-figure paintings of the period.

No. 30 was the cause of a celebrated art scandal of the 1750's. In 1759, Sir Richard Grosvenor commissioned Hogarth to paint a theme of his own choice, and Hogarth, angered by the sale of No. 30 in the preceding year to Sir Thomas Sebright for £404 as a Correggio, determined to paint his own *Sigismunda* for an equally high price. Sir Richard Grosvenor rejected the painting (now in the Tate Gallery), and in a rage, Hogarth prepared a subscription ticket for it in 1761 showing *Time Smoking a Picture* intended to ridicule the false values attached even to mis-attributed Italian pictures. Horace Walpole, who had called Furini's *Sigismunda* "one of the finest pictures in England" said that Hogarth's version was no more "like Sigismunda than I to Hercules . . . (and that) Hogarth's performance was more ridiculous than anything he ever ridiculed." (Saxl-Wittkower, Wind, Antal, *op. cit.*)

LORENZO LIPPI   1606-Florence-1665

In addition to Baldinucci's life of Lippi, there is also a brief manuscript life by Giovanni Camillo Sagrestani of 1731 in the Biblioteca Nazionale at Florence which adds little to our knowledge of his painting. Lippi studied initially with Matteo Rosselli, who soon acknowledged Lippi's precocious talent for what Baldinucci called "his pure imitation of reality" ("del vero"). Such was Lippi's devotion to the works of Santi di Tito that he continued to copy them through-out his life, and along with Curradi, Lippi was responsible for the survival of Santi di Tito's simplified Counter-Reformation imagery well into the seventeenth century. Rosselli's influence is apparent however in Lippi's painting, and it seems likely that he entered the Rosselli studio at precisely the period when his master was himself evincing signs of an increased observation of nature as in *The Triumph of David* of 1620 or *The Three Youths condemned to the Furnace* both in the Pitti. Lippi however stripped his paintings of the elaborately-patterned fabrics and lavish decorative accessories still in fashion in the early 1620's to achieve greater simplicity, as in his *Samson and Delilah* (Stockholm, National Museum) of *circa* 1630, the year in which he registered in the Accademia del Disegno. *The Martyrdom of St. Andrew* painted for San Frediano in 1639 is Lippi's first known signed and dated painting and shows him as the master of an unvarnished naturalism paralleled only in the contemporary work of Giovanni Martinelli (see no. 37). The artist's first period is concluded with his visit of around 1643-4 to Innsbruck where he worked for the archduchess of Austria, Claudia de' Medici and her court: the beautiful lunettes in the Ardinghelli Chapel in S. Gaetano immediately precede this. Sagrestani says that Lippi was "much loved" by Cardinal Carlo de' Medici, and he was sufficiently esteemed at court to be allocated the design of tapestries (with Vignali) for the Grand Ducal audience room in Palazzo Pitti which were woven in 1643.

Of all Florentine artists, Lippi was the one who formed the closest friendship with Salvator Rosa during his Tuscan period of 1640-1649. Rosa, who assisted Lippi with the landscape in a *Flight into Egypt*, was probably most attracted by Lippi's literary activities, in which Lippi's spirited personality best expressed itself. Lippi's *Il Malmantile raquistato*, a "comic pendant" to the heroic *Gerusalemme Liberata* by Tasso, was probably written under Rosa's influence, and although not published until 1676 was circulated in manuscript form in Lippi's lifetime.

31 *Angelica tending the wounded Medoro*

Oil on canvas, 173 by 238 cms.

PROVENANCE: Marchese Mattias Maria Bartolommei, Florence (?), Joseph Leeson, later 1st Earl of Milltown.

LITERATURE: Baldinucci, 1847, V, p. 270; Bigongiari, 1974, p. 43, repr. fig. 6 (as Vignali), Wynn, 1974, p. 108, repr. fig. 7 (as Vignali).

The painting illustrates Ludovico Ariosto's *Orlando Furioso*, XIX, 12-19. Medoro, follower of the Moorish leader Dardinello was wounded in the battle before Paris. Angelica, a princess of Cathay found him, and ". . . having learned of Surgerie the art . . . by skill she had in juyce of herbs and flowers/ for to renew Medoro's lively powers" (Harrington translation, 1591)—cured him. The couple fell in love and were married. In the background of the picture are seen the dead body of Medoro's companion Cloridano and the horse which Angelica borrowed from a shepherd.

Formerly attributed to Vignali, the painting's style, its solid areas of colour and the facial appearance of the models point firmly to Lippi's authorship. Baldinucci (op. cit.) states that the Marchese Bartolemmei had two "quadri da sala" by Lippi showing stories from Ariosto, and this may be one of these. Baldinucci tells how Agnolo Galli commissioned Lippi to paint a *Triumph of David* including portraits of all of Galli's seventeen children: this picture was shown in the exhibition *Tesori segreti delle case fiorentini* (1960), and a version with fewer figures is in the Pitti (Sricchia, 1963). From these two paintings it is possible to identify the features of Galli's daughters: generally speaking they all had long necks, high foreheads, small mouths and long, softly-outlined noses very similar to that of Angelica in this painting and identical with the models for Nos. 32 and 33. The model for Angelica also appears in Lippi's *St. Cosma* (Florence, private collection: Sricchia, 1963, fig. 44). Possibly under the influence of Salvator Rosa, Lippi began to take a greater interest in landscape after 1640, including a landscape comparable with this one in his *Christ and the Woman of Samaria* of 1644 (Vienna, Kunsthistorisches Museum). This and a comparison with the treatment of the *Musical Angels* in S. Gaetano suggests a dating in the early 1640's.

National Gallery of Ireland, Dublin.

32 *An Allegory of Innocence*

Oil on canvas, (oval) 74 by 59cms.

LITERATURE: McCorquodale, 1979 (b).

The iconography of this figure corresponds exactly with *Innocence* as described in Cesare Ripa's *Iconologia* (Ripa, 1603, p. 235): "A young virgin (*Verginella*), dressed in white, wearing on her head a garland of flowers, with a lamb in her arms."

A comparison with the portraits of Agnolo Galli's daughters in Lippi's *Triumph of David* (see no. 31) formerly in the Galli-Tassi Collection, Florence, shows that the model for *Innocence* was one of these girls. Baldinucci writes that Lippi painted "small pictures" of six of Galli's daughters—*Innocence* and *Fortune* (no. 33), *Music* (Florence, Private Collection), *St. Agatha* (Paris, Moratilla Collection), *St. Cosma* (Florence, Private Collection) and *An Allegory* (Angers, Musée) may be these pictures.

In terms of its colours, *Innocence* is one of Lippi's most pleasing paintings and perfectly illustrates his "simple imitation of the natural" (Baldinucci), his solid modelling of form and the simple but varied outlines of his figures.

Visitors of the Ashmolean Museum, Oxford

33   *An Allegory of Fortune*

Oil on canvas, 76 by 63.8 cms.

LITERATURE: McCorquodale, 1979 (b).

As a rule (see no. 32) Lippi adhered quite closely to Ripa's codification of iconography, but he does not appear to have done so in this instance, and no precise explanation for the allegory is possible. The young woman is dressed as a gypsy, and would therefore appear to be using the playing cards to tell a fortune. In the background, however, sits a monkey, who also holds the cards with one paw. Monkeys are described in Ripa (1764) as being "of all the animals the one which seems best to understand the affairs of men", and are traditionally associated with either trickery or mimicry of human actions. A monkey appears in the frontispiece engraved by Francesco Zuccherelli to Lippi's design for the 1731 and 1750 editions of Lippi's *Il Malmantile raquistato*, apparently in the role of mimicry: it is possible that this painting illustrates one of the innumerable Tuscan proverbs on which Lippi drew in his poetry.

One of the most strikingly Caravaggesque of Lippi's half-length single figures, it recalls particularly certain paintings by Artemesia Gentileschi such as *St. Catherine* (Florence, Opeficio delle Pietre Dure: Sricchia, 1963). The model was one of the daughters of Agnolo Galli, and the painting may be one of the "small pictures" of six of the Galli girls mentioned by Baldinucci (see no. 31). Her face is identical with that of the Angers *Allegory*.

Ulster Museum, Belfast

GIOVANNI BATTISTA LUPICINI

1575-Florence-1648

Baldinucci did not devote a life to Lupicini, but mentions him as briefly follows in his life of Cesare Dandini: "It was in the year 1625, when a pupil of Cigoli's, called Giovambatista Lupicini who was widely esteemed for his copies of the great masters, was commissioned to go to Pisa, to copy there many of the beautiful pictures in the cathedral: and because this involved much work, Giovambatista wished to take an assistant." He selected Dandini. (Baldinucci, 1846, IV. p. 554). Apart from the signed *Martha reproving Mary* (Vienna Kunsthistorisches Museum) no other secure work by Lupicini is known, and even his dates are based to some extent on conjecture, although the records of the Accademia del Disegno show that he was dead by 1648. All subsequent attributions to Lupicini are there based on a comparison with the Vienna picture, which, however has a very distinctive style indicating that Lupicini's sources lay in the realism of artists like Martinelli and Lippi.

34   *The Repentant Magdalen contemplating the Cross*

Oil on canvas, 52 by 39 cms.

A French tradition asserts that St. Mary Magdalen (see no. 14) was set adrift by infidels in a rudderless boat with her sister Martha and Lazarus and, arriving at Marseilles, converted the Gauls and did penance in the wilderness for thirty years fed by celestial food. It is in her role of penitent that she is shown here, contemplating a roughly-made cross.

Formerly attributed to Cigoli, this painting can be securely given to Lupicini for stylistic reasons. A comparison with *Martha reproving Mary* (Vienna, Kunsthistorisches Museum) and an *Allegory of Painting* (Columbia Museum of Art) attributed to Lupicini by Ewald (1965). The Columbia painting has the same flowing curls as No. 34.

P. & D. Colnaghi and Co.

GIOVANNI MANNOZZI, *called* GIOVANNI DA SAN GIOVANNI

1592 S. Giovanni Valdarno-1636 Florence

Giovanni da San Giovanni is best known for his numerous lively and colourful fresco decorations throughout Tuscany, and Baldinucci describes his spirited personality at length. Trained by Matteo Rosselli, himself an able frescoist, he registered in the Accademia del Disegno in 1612, and his earliest fresco dates from 1616. His *Martyrdom of St. Blaise* of 1619 (Montepulciano, S. Agnese) is still dependent on Rosselli, and in the same year he frescoed the famous facade of Palazzo dell'Antella in Piazza S. Croce, including a copy of Caravaggio's *Sleeping Cupid*. Giovanni's natural inclination to a less 'official' art than that of many of his contemporaries was undoubtedly encouraged by his contact with Northern artists such as Callot and Filippo Napoletano, both of whom were at the court of Cosimo II: his experience of the Bamboccianti in Rome in 1623-4 and 1627 further confirmed his anti-academicism. His Roman masterpiece is the apse fresco in the SS. Quattro Coronati, and his answer to the Bolognese classicism of Reni's *Aurora* is the deliberately informal *Night* also for the Rospigliosi.

On his return to Florence, Giovanni established a reputation as the leading fresco decorator of his day, and apart from works in many villas, palaces, and churches, painted canvases with unconventional renderings of unusual themes such as *Venus combing Cupid's hair for fleas* (Florence, Pitti) and *The Wedding Night* (Pitti). In 1635, he obtained the commission from the Grand Duke Ferdinando II to fresco the Sala terrena of Palazzo Pitti with a series showing *The Apotheosis of the Medici Family*, which was completed after his death by Furini, Cecco Bravo and Vannini.

35 *Pievano Arlotto playing a Practical Joke on Some Huntsmen*

Oil on canvas, 102 by 145 cms.

PROVENANCE: Grazini Family, Florence; William Kent; Sir Nathaniel Curzon, 1st Baron Scarsdale, 1758

LITERATURE: Baldinucci, 1846, IV. p. 243; Walpole, 1768 (1928), p. 64; Young, 1771, I, p. 194; Cambiagi, 1774, IX, p. 159; Kedleston Catalogue, pre-1787; Waagen, 1838, p. 393; Giglioli, 1949, p. 153 (among missing works); Briganti, 1953, pp. 46-49, fig. 25; Banti-Mannini, 1977, No. 32, fig. 55

The parish priest ("pievano") Arlotto Mainardi was noted for his practical jokes, another of which was illustrated by Volterrano (Florence, Pitti).

In a letter to Sir Nathaniel Curzon from his picture dealer William Kent dated 15th August 1758 from northern Italy, this picture is mentioned along with eight others as having been purchased for a total of £1015. There appears to be no mention anywhere of the Arnaldi or Pallavicini provenances mentioned by Briganti (op. cit.). The painting appears in Robert Adam's section for the Music Room at Kedleston dated 1760, in which it was hung from c. 1762. It is referred to in Kedleston catalogues from 1769 onwards as "*Horses, Figures, &c*", although Kent specifically noted that it was the picture referred to by Baldinucci (information kindly supplied by Mr. Leslie Harris).

One of the best examples of Giovanni da San Giovanni's satirical realism, it is tempting to see in it the influence of the Bamboccianti (Briganti, *op. cit.*), the group of Northern artists working in Rome around Pieter van Laer (1592/5-1642) and painting scenes of low-life with brigands, peasants and soldiers. Briganti suggests that No. 34 may even have been painted in Rome.

Viscount Scarsdale, Kedleston Hall, Derbyshire

36   *Madonna and Child with the Infant St. John*

Fresco, 95 by 70.5 cms.

PROVENANCE: Marchese Riccardi (?) Florence; The Rev. John Sanford

LITERATURE: Sanford Collection, Yates' List, 1838, No. 12; Sanford Catalogue, 1847, No. 40;
Waagen, 1857 (Supplement), IV. p. 398; Corsham Catalogue, 1891, No. 99;
Corsham Catalogue, 1903, No. 48

No. 36 was acquired by the Rev. Sanford for £32 10s 0d from the Marchese Riccardi, and was supposed to have been painted for the Riccardi Palace in Florence. The wide success of Giovanni da San Giovanni's frescoes on a large scale may have led to the demand for such portable 'frescoes' often on terracotta, which also recall the street tabernacles which were among his first works.

The style of this fresco recalls that of the painter's master Rosselli, but also derives from Poccetti and the Florentine High Renaissance.

Lent from the Methuen Collection

GIOVANNI MARTINELLI

1610-Florence-1659

Dr. Stella Rudolph will show in a forthcoming article on Martinelli that he did not in fact die in 1668, as has previously been thought. Baldinucci did not write his life, and apart from mentions in guidebooks of the eighteenth century and subsequent writers such as Lanzi, few earlier records can be drawn upon in an appreciation of his importance. In 1634, Martinelli painted the five fresco lunettes in the SS. Annunziata at Pistoia, showing the life of the Blessed Buonaventura Bonaccorsi, and in the following year registered in the Accademia del Disegno. The Pistoia lunettes, although dependent on the precedent of Poccetti introduce far greater variety through landscape, colour and carefully-observed poses and gesture. In 1642-3 Martinelli painted frescoes in S. Cecelia, Florence and in 1650, painted the processional banner with the *Assumption* for the Compagnia di Prato. Martinelli seems to have developed a realistic style in the 1630s based on the type of Caravaggesque sources used by Cesare Dandini on occasions: although very different from Dandini in intention, many of Martinelli's figures share a metallic posed quality similar to Dandini's, with the same total lack of dramatic action. Attributions to him can often be made on the basis of comparison with his masterpiece *The Miracle of the Mule* (Pescia, S. Francesco), or *Belshazzar's Feast* (Florence, Uffizi) with its sumptuous metal vases and wide range of characteristic facial types. Martinelli seems to have worked almost exclusively for private patrons, although never for the Medici.

37   *The Sacrifice of Noah*

Oil on canvas, 129.5 by 173 cms.

LITERATURE: McCorquodale, 1979 (b).

The painting illustrates Genesis, VIII; 20. After the Flood, the Ark was left high and dry on the mountains of Ararat, and, on being commanded to leave the Ark by God with his family and all the animals, Noah made a burnt offering of "every clean beast, and of every clean fowl."

A major addition to Martinelli's *oeuvre*, this painting is a fine example of his mature style. Characteristic of him is the allover dark tonality, out of which the flesh tones emerge with a slightly metallic effect, the "frozen" composition with no real sense of movement and the careful distinction between the different ages of the participants: in this respect the aged, standing woman with her leathery, wrinkled skin is typical. The two young women are virtually identical to those in *Belshazzar's Feast*, with whom they have in common long, tapering fingers and—a typical Martinelli device—ribbons wound into the hair.

No date can be assigned to No. 37 until much more is known about Martinelli. Although Martinelli was clearly investigating the possibilities of naturalism at the same time as Lippi (Sricchia, 1953), his results are totally different (see Nos. 31-33). Another version of this painting is in a Scottish private collection.

Sir Francis Dashwood, Bt.

38 *Portrait of a Girl*

Oil on canvas, 50.5 by 44cms.

Previously attributed to Furini, this charming study is certainly by Martinelli: apart from the characteristic paint handling, the use of a red ribbon in the hair is frequently found in his female heads.

Private Collection

SEBASTIANO MAZZONI
c. 1611 Florence-1678 Venice

Mazzoni's was one of the more complex artistic personalities produced by 17th century Florence: as much a poet as a painter, he was forced into what he describes in one of his poems as "an exile from the City of Flowers" after satirizing some important figure. The date of his birth has been calculated from an archival entry stating that he died in 1678 at the age of about 67, which renders somewhat dubious the Venetian biographer Temanza's assertion that he studied with Cristofano Allori (died 1621). 1611 was also the year of Simone Pignoni's birth, and it was his sensuous style together with those of Furini and Cecco Bravo which formed Mazzoni's. He was in Venice by 1649 when he dated one of his large paintings in S. Benedetto. In Venice, he came under the influence of Fetti and Strozzi, whose loose, painterly handling he developed to an even greater degree of spontaneity and *bravura*. He appears to have derived his figure types and highly dramatic poses principally from Cecco Bravo, to whom several paintings formerly attributed to Mazzoni are now given. Short and ugly in appearance, Mazzoni increasingly made use of bizarre elements, hyper-active figures and spiteful satire. His deliberate exploitation of disturbing visual effects is best seen in *The Dream of Pope Onorio III* (Venice, S. Maria del Carmine) and *The Death of Cleopatra* (Rovigo, Accademia dei Concordi). Several later 17th century Venetian painters were influenced by him, including Niccolò Bambini, Andrea Celesti and Sebastiano Ricci.

39 *Susanna and the Elders*

Oil on canvas, 162.6 by 125.8cm. Signed, lower right "*Mazzoni (?Fior) faciebat 1649*" (remainder illegible).

For the story of Susanna, see No. 9. This is a particularly important addition to our knowledge of Mazzoni's style at the presumed time of his arrival in Venice, since it was painted in the same year as his *S. Benedict in Glory among the Theological Virtues* (Venice, S. Benedetto). A monogrammed *Lucretia* was recently exhibited in London (Heim Gallery, *The Baroque in Italy*, Summer 1978, No. 11) which shows something of Furini's influence, whereas No. 39 is close to Pignoni (see Nos. 44-47). The face of Susanna is similar to that of the Virgin in *St. Benedict presenting a Priest to the Virgin* in S. Benedetto, and her languid *contrapposto* recalls the more extreme movement of the figure of *Faith* in the same picture. Particularly reminiscent of Furini and Pignoni are the long strokes of liquid paint used to create the effect of shimmering folds of drapery.

Private Collection

LIVIO MEHUS

Although Flemish by birth, Mehus escaped from the Thirty Years' War with his family to Milan when very young, and studied there with the Dutch battle-painter Carlo Fiammingo. Baldinucci describes how Mehus's spirited nature led him to leave Milan at the age of fifteen to go to Rome. Introduced to the Medici family on the way, he realized his ambition to work with a leading Roman painter, Pietro da Cortona, but did so in Florence, assisting Cortona in his decorations in the Sala di Marte at the Pitti Palace (1645-6). After three years in Genoa and Piedmont, he returned to Florence and entered the service of the Grand Duke. In 1650, he was in Rome with Stefano della Bella, and he made other journeys to Rome and to Venice, all of which broadened an already highly individual talent based primarily on a combination of Flemish realism, Cortona's decorative manner and the languor of Correggio. His style represents the trends which emerge in Florence around 1670 in the works of Pietro Dandini and Alessandro Gherardini, where a move towards a less insular approach is evident.

40-43   *Four Landscapes*

Each, oil on canvas, 49.5 by 65 cms.

LITERATURE: Chiarini, 1978 (b), figs. 4-7

Chiarini (*op. cit.*) notes that only recently has attention been paid to Mehus' activity as a landscape painter, despite Baldinucci's having mentioned his landscapes for the Cavalier Ambra and Paolo Falconierei in Rome. On the basis of comparison with other documented pictures, Chiarini dates these four landscapes to 1675-85, pointing out that they break completely with the Florentine sceneographic landscape traditions initiated by Crescenzio Onofri: he also draws attention to their protoromantic lyricism deriving from Rosa and anticipating Peruzzini, Magnasco, Marco Ricci and the Rococo.

Lent by courtesy of Viscount Coke

SIMONE PIGNONI 1611-Florence-1698

Baldinucci only mentions Pignoni briefly in passing in his lives of other painters, but Pignoni's pupil Giovanni Camillo Sagrestani devoted a short life to him. According to Baldinucci, Pignoni's first master was Fabrizio Boschi, followed by Passignano, but the most important influence on his painting was his close study of Furini, with whose work Pignoni's is often confused. Pignoni's chronology is still unclear, although his two major altarpieces, *St. Louis providing a Banquet for the Poor* of 1682 (Florence, S. Felicità) and the *Madonna in Glory with Saints* placed in SS. Annunziata in 1671 provide secure points of reference. Although Pignoni's voluptuous female nudes are superficially the same as Furini's, in general they are heavier and all share the same oval face, heavy-lidded eyes and open mouth; apart from Furini, Pignoni derived his type of nude from the works of Titian, Reni and Albani which he saw on a visit to Lombardy. The proliferation of such nudes tends to obscure his more original paintings, such as the brilliant *David and Abigail* in the Bigongiari Collection, Florence. Pignoni's use of heavy chiaroscuro and *sfumato* effects probably influenced Dolci's best pupil, Onorio Marinari to move away from Dolci's style, and in some ways Marinari brought the Pignoni manner to its finest conclusion in his *Vision of S. Maria Maddalena de' Pazzi* (Florence, S. Maria Maggiore). Pignoni was prepared to abandon his *sfumato* effects in official commissions like the *St. Louis*, which was greatly admired by Giordano, but which lacks conviction and shows Pignoni attempting a Baroque grandeur beyond his reach. His pupil, Francesco Botti closely imitated Pignoni's style.

44   *St. Sebastian*

Oil on canvas, (octagonal), 81 by 73.5 cms.

St. Sebastian was a young nobleman of Narbonne in Gaul who commanded a company of the Praetorian Guard of the Emperor Diocletian. The latter failed to persuade Sebastian to renounce his Christian faith, and had him shot with arrows. This failed to kill him, and St. Irene found him and tended his wounds, but subsequently Diocletian had him clubbed to death. After SS. Peter and Paul, he is the third saint of Rome.

Formerly attributed to Furini, No. 44 is stylistically closer to the early Pignoni. A comparison with Pignoni's *Madonna* in a Florentine Private Collection (Cantelli, 1977) reveals a similar handling of paint, less fluid than Furini's and suggesting that the artist might even have studied Ficherelli (cfr. No. 27).

Guildhall Art Gallery

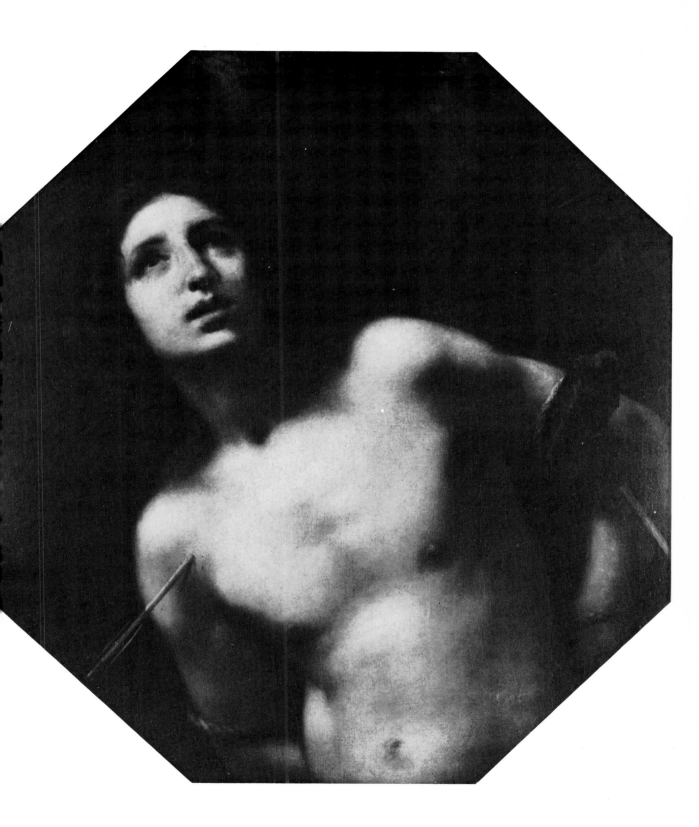

45 *St. Praxedis*

Oil on canvas, 92 by 74cms.

PROVENANCE: The Torrie Collection
LITERATURE: Notes and Queries, No. 295, June 23, 1885, Vol XI. Series I, p. 486 (as by Carlo Dolci)

St. Praxedis's name is usually linked with that of St. Pudentiana, and although a church was dedicated to her in the 4th century, mention is first made of her in 7th century itineraries to the Roman Catacombs. This painting illustrates the grim legend associated with St. Praxedis, in which she collected the blood of Christian martyrs and buried their mutilated remains.

Formerly attributed to Carlo Dolci and described as "*A Roman Lady pressing her Lover's Heart*" (i.e. *Sigismunda*, see No. 30) this is a version by Pignoni of what appears to have been one of his most popular paintings. An almost identical version is in the Ponce Art Museum, Puerto Rico (Nissman, 1969) and a slightly reduced version was sold as a *St. Cecilia* attributed to Furini in the Gasch Sale, Dresden, 29th April, 1912.

With typical ambiguity, Pignoni shows the saint as a solitary nocturnal heroine, voluptuous and lavishly attired, who performs her task languidly and without revulsion: this is the antithesis of the most famous rendering of this theme in Florence, by Ficherelli.

The Ponce version has been dated to the 1660's for stylistic reasons (Cantelli, 1974), showing as it does an almost complete liberation on Pignoni's part from the Furini manner: there seems no reason to suppose a dating later than 1670 for No. 45.

Private Collection

46 *The Mystic Marriage of St. Catherine of Alexandria*

Oil on canvas, 132 by 155cms.

PROVENANCE: Foggini family, Florence 1729 (?); Ignazio Hugford; Henry Blundell of Ince, 1779

LITERATURE: Ewald, 1964 (a). p, 225, notes 29 and 33; McCorquodale, 1974, p. 207, repr. pl. 12

EXHIBITED: Florence, Accademici del Disegno, 1767, p. 24; Liverpool, 1960, No. 28

St. Catherine was a 3rd century saint born of noble, possibly even royal parents in Alexandria. After her baptism as a Christian, Christ appeared to her in a dream and made her His celestial spouse by slipping a ring on her finger. When she awoke, she found the ring and kept it for the remainder of her life. (See No. 13).

This is a slightly smaller version with minimal variations of Pignoni's painting of the theme in a Florentine private collection, which was engraved as Plate CIX of volume II of Lastri's *Etruria Pittrice* (1795) when it was in the Rucellai Collection (Ewald, op. cit. fig. 40). The picture evidently enjoyed considerable popularity, since apart from this version by Pignoni himself, it was copied by other painters: among these copies are examples in the Nemes Collection, Budapest (Ewald, op. cit.), Carrara Museum and the Dashwood Collection, West Wycombe Park.

Although no satisfactory chronology has yet been proposed for Pignoni's painting, the style of this painting is close to that of the SS. Annunziata altarpiece (see above) of 1671, and to Pignoni's masterpiece, *David and Abigail*: in each, Pignoni achieved luxurious surface texture by means of flickering highlights (such as those on St. Catherine's dress) and a combination of crisp detail with soft *sfumato* in the faces. The whole figure of St. Catherine is still indebted however to Furini's experiments with shimmering surfaces and languorous gestures, but the more generalized treatment of flesh is wholly characteristic of Pignoni.

Private Collection

47 *An Allegorical Scene*

Oil on canvas, 45 by 25cm.

EXHIBITED: London, Heim Gallery, 1967, *Baroque sketches, drawings and sculptures*, No. 5a (as by Volterrano)

In the lower part of the painting, a laurel-crowned youth nestles against Venus, who is recognisable by her attendant white doves. At the left, Cupid releases an arrow in the couple's direction. Above, another male figure holding a large book with his left hand is guided upwards towards Jupiter by Hercules in his role of Heroic Virtue (Ripa) and crowned by Glory, who also corresponds to Ripa's iconographical description. The inclusion of music-making nymphs around a fountain in a garden recalls Rinaldo's amorous ensnarement by Armida in Tasso's *Gerusalemme Liberata*, Canto XVI, which also includes descriptions of doves: since however several of the other usual iconographical details of this scene are missing, it seems unlikely to show Rinaldo with Armida. An alternative interpretation may be the following: the youth in Venus's arms may be Tasso himself (since as a poet he is entitled to a laurel crown) inspired by the goddess of Love to write his epic poem, part of which enfolds itself in the background. Even before the publication of *Gerusalemme Liberata* in 1581, Tasso began to doubt his own religious orthodoxy, presenting himself to the Inquisition for examination. Thereafter, he not only revised his poem as *Gerusalemme conquistata* (1593) but under the impact of Counter-Reformation morality "reformed" his later writings. This may be symbolised by his "redemption" at the hands of Heroic Virtue and Glory in the upper scene, where the central figure is certainly that of an older man. The relationship of such an iconography to Pietro da Cortona's ceiling frescoes in the Planetary Rooms of Palazzo Pitti cannot be overlooked, notably in the Sala di Venere, where the theme is *Pallas tearing a youth from the arms of Venus*. In this scene, Pallas (i.e. Minerva) brings the youth through the heavens to Hercules, also seen there as Heroic Virtue.

Although reminscent of Volterrano, this painting is closer in certain details such as the figures of Venus, the youth and Glory, to Pignoni. Apparently a *bozzetto* for a larger canvas or a fresco, it derives from Luca Giordano's *Allegory of the Peace between Florence and Fiesole* (Florence, Pitti) probably painted between 1682 and 1685. No. 47 follows the Giordano very carefully, substituting Venus for the figure of the Arno and the central fountain for the view of Florence, but retaining the position and pose of Jupiter and the upper right-hand group. This derivation, and a comparison with Pignoni's replica of his altarpiece showing *St. Louis providing a Banquet for the Poor* of 1682 for S. Felicità (Florence, Pitti) point to Pignoni's authorship. Giordano admired Pignoni's work, and Pignoni was in turn indebted to Giordano's Florentine paintings. Another similar, but slightly larger composition with considerable variations in detail, is in the Paul Ganz Collection, New York.

Private Collection

GIOVANNI CAMILLO SAGRESTANI

According to Gabburri, Sagrestani first studied with Antonio Giusti and Romolo Panfi, after which he travelled to Rome, Venice, Parma and finally Bologna where he studied with Carlo Cignani. He made great use of engravings, especially after Simon Vouet, to whose work he was particularly devoted, and whose luminosity plays a considerable part in Sagrestani's own effects. Gabburri attacks Sagrestani for his lack of *disegno* and places him at the beginning of Florentine painting's decline, but nonetheless it was he who introduced Late Baroque decorative concepts into Florence: his ecclesiastical and secular frescoes are directly indebted to Giordano's Florentine work. Very few pictures can be securely attributed to Sagrestani: of those which can, the finest is his *Marriage of the Virgin* (Florence, S. Spirito). This was installed in 1713, by which time Sagrestani's style already bore resemblances to that of his pupil Matteo Bonechi. However, its reliance on strong, sudden lighting, brilliant colour, and dramatic compositional effects enhanced by elongated figures permit the salient features of his style to be recognised in his many other canvases.

48 *An Episode in the Life of S. Verdiana*

Oil on canvas, 46 by 32 cms.

A *bozzetto* for Sagrestani's painting of this theme in the Confraternità della Misericordia, Castelfiorentino, No. 48 varies only slightly in detail from the finished picture (see Arte in Valdelsa, 119-20). Sagrestani also painted a series of oval canvases for the Confraternity showing scenes from the Saint's life.

Brinsley Ford, Esq.

49 *The Pietà with Angels*

Oil on canvas, 44.5 by 34.3 cms.

LITERATURE: Wilson Frothingham, 1968, pp. 210-11, fig 1

This appears to be the *bozzetto* for the painting of the same theme in the Uffizi, which measures 145 by 111.5cms. (Ewald, 1974, Cat. No. 184, fig. 184). Ewald suggests that the Uffizi picture may form part of a series showing the life of the Virgin, since two other paintings, *The Marriage of the Virgin* and *The Annunciation* also belong to the Florentine Galleries. Frothingham (op cit.) points out that the composition provided the Florentine sculptor Massimiliano Soldani Benzi (1656-1740) with the inspiration for a similar group which he executed first in wax, then in bronze, and subsequently copied in porcelain. It is of course much more likely that Soldani-Benzi knew the larger, and more finished canvas. A fine version of the group in white Doccia porcelain was included in the exhibition *The Twilight of the Medici*, Cat. No. 246 (see Bibliography).

Private Collection

50 *The Virgin with St. John*

Oil on canvas, 25.3 by 19 cms.

EXHIBITED: Hazlitt Gallery 1963, *17th and 18th century Italian Paintings*, No. 18, Pl. 7c.

This is a *bozzetto* for a slightly larger *Crucifixion* by Sagrestani (41.3 by 28.6 cms.) formerly in the Marshall Collection. The latter has an arched top and measured 41.3 by 28.6 cms. and in it, the two figures of the Virgin and St. John were posed exactly as in No. 50 on either side of the crucified Christ.

Private Collection

JUSTUS SUSTERMANS 1597 Antwerp-1681 Florence

At around the age of twenty, Sustermans went to Paris and entered the studio of François Pourbus the Younger (1569-1622), who was also Flemish, and who directed him towards his career as a portraitist. After three years, he went to Florence, where he began his sixty-one years' service to the Medici court under Cosimo II and his descendants. Although his principal activity was as a portraitist, Sustermans also painted animals, genre, some historical pictures and the occasional religious theme—all of which recall his Flemish origins. Rubens was a great admirer of his work and a lifelong friend, sending Sustermans his *Consequences of War* in 1638 (Florence, Pitti), but although Sustermans often evoked Rubens and Van Dyck in his likenesses, many of his portraits strike a more domestic note than theirs. It is to him that we owe our knowledge of the unfortunate physiognomy of almost every member of the Medici family in the 17th century, although his acclaim brought him commissions to travel to Innsbruck, Vienna, Rome, Parma, Modena and Mantua. His reputation has been dulled by the poor copies after his originals, and at his best he ranks as one of the best 17th century portraitists: his contact with works by the finest of his contemporaries (including Velazquez) ensured his lead over many lesser painters, and his often profound studies of character such as *Galileo* or *Pandolfo Ricasoli* (both Pitti) are intensely memorable.

51   *Portrait of a Lady*

Oil on canvas, 134.6 by 88.9 cms.

PROVENANCE: Panciatichi-Ximines family, Florence; W. B. Spencer; R. S. Holford; Sir George Holford

LITERATURE: Catalogue of the Holford Collection, Westonbirt. Volume, 1924, no. 79, fig. LXIX

EXHIBITED: Burlington House, 1887, no. 6 (as Van Dyck); Royal Academy, 1893, no. 114; Royal Academy, 1908, no. 121; Burlington Fine Art Club, 1921, no. 18; Royal Academy, 1927, no. 158; Royal Academy, *17th Century Art in Europe*, 1938, no. 74; Royal Academy, 1953-4, no. 262

Although perhaps not freely painted enough to justify the old attribution to Van Dyck, the refinement of handling is wholly characteristic of Sustermans at his best. Traditionally called *A Medici Princess*, the sitter bears no resemblance to any known member of the Medici family.

Private Collection

52 *The Senators of Florence swearing allegiance to Ferdinando II*

Oil on canvas, 61 by 82cms.

PROVENANCE: Valentino Farinola, Florence, 1677
LITERATURE: Bocchi-Cinelli, 1677, p. 269; Gualandi, 1844, V. p. 86, No. 167; Bautier, 1912, pp. 13-15; Winner, 1963, p. 243, fig. 25; Campbell, 1977, p. 68, note 19
EXHIBITED: Milan Finarte, April-May 1972, No. 13

This is a *bozzetto* for Sustermans' huge painting of the theme which hung as an overdoor in the lunette above the *porta principale* of the so-called Sala delle Nicchie in the Pitti Palace (Winner, Campbell, op. cit.). Baldinucci describes it in considerable detail, identifying several of the figures: Ferdinando II is seated on the throne, with at his right, the Archduchess Maria Maddalena and at the left Christine of Lorraine. At Ferdinando's feet kneels Senator Bartolomeo Concini, while the master of ceremonies from Florence Cathedral holds open the Gospels for the swearing of the oath. Other senators and ambassadors are also present. The painting, which had been added to at the top to transform it into a rectangle, hung for many years in the Uffizi library, and is now being restored.

According to Bocchi-Cinelli (op. cit.), this *bozzetto* belonged to Valentino Farinola, 'Auditore di Camera' of the Grand Duke. The event depicted took place in 1618, when Ferdinando was eight years old.

Visitors of the Ashmolean Museum, Oxford

FILIPPO TARCHIANI

Before 1580?-Florence-after 1643?

Tarchiani is one of the least studied of Florentine 17th century painters, and any attributions to him must be made on the basis of a comparison with his *Paul III visiting Michelangelo in his Studio* of 1616-17 (Florence, Casa Buonarotti), *The Stoning of St. Stephen* of 1621 (Capraia, S. Stefano), and *The Baptism of Christ* of 1627 now in S. Margherita de' Ricci, Florence. His late style is exemplified by *A Miracle of S. Verdiana* (1631-3: Castelfiorentino, S. Francesco). Baldinucci scarcely mentions him, but says that he was impressed by the style of Pagani, whose studio he frequented. A note in the 'libro degli Accademici del Disegno' indicates that Tarchiani was in Rome from 1601-7. Although his style bears superficial resemblances to Rosselli's at times, it is on the whole more sensitive and refined, and he had greater ability for composition. The range of his sources was probably very wide, and he came into contact with Giovanni da San Giovanni when he assisted with the decoration of the Palazzo Antella in 1619.

53   *The Rest on the Flight into Egypt*

Oil on canvas, 80 by 115.5cm.

EXHIBITED: London, Royal Academy, 1950-51, *Works by Holbein and other Masters of the 16th and 17th Centuries*, No. 415 (as by Rosselli)

The Pseudo Matthew relates that on their way through the desert, the Holy Family sought shelter from the sun beneath a palm tree which the Child commanded to bend so that Mary could pick its fruit. When the tree righted itself, it miraculously revealed a spring. In this picture, the Virgin and Child are being served by angels. In the basket may be the Roses of Jericho, supposed to have sprung up wherever the Holy Family rested during the Flight.

Although not unlike Rosselli's style in certain respects, No. 53 can be attributed to Tarchiani for stylistic reasons. A comparison may be made with the three versions of *Supper at Emmaus* (Munich, Alte Pinakothek, Los Angeles, County Museum and Castle Forbes and Balforbes, Lord Forbes) which is clearly by the same hand, and with which Tarchiani's name has been connected (see Steingräber, 1975, p. 35). These have previously been attributed to Empoli.

Private Collection

JACOPO VIGNALI

1592-Pratovecchio-1664 Florence

Although Baldinucci failed to write a life of Vignali, Sebastiano Benedetto Bartolozzi published one in the 18th century based on letters and the artist's account book. Vignali, one of the most poetic and sensitive of Florentine painters, entered Rosselli's studio as early as 1605 when he was only thirteen—a precocity not unlike that of his own famous pupil, Carlo Dolci. From 1615-28, Vignali was involved in the decorations of the Casa Buonarroti, and registered at the Accademia del Disegno in 1622. His *Jacob's Dream* in the Casa Buonarroti is derived from Cigoli (see No. 5) and this influence together with Artemisa Gentilesch's led him away from Rosselli's slightly dull style towards his own deeply emotional works of the 1620's—such as *Christ showing his wounds to St. Bernard* (1623, Florence, S. Simone) or *The Agony in the Garden* of 1626 (Castellina, S. Lucia). The latter, painted at the time when Dolci entered Vignali's studio, is the starting point for Dolci's art. Apart from his many altarpieces such as *S. Liborio* (Florence, S. Jacopo Soprarno) and *The Mystical Communion of Blessed Clara of Montefalco* (Florence, S. Spirito). Vignali's masterpieces are the two small canvases showing the *Magdalen* and *St. Margaret* (Florence, SS. Annunziata), which show him painting in a style which appears to owe something to Guercino, to whom many of his pictures have been wrongly attributed in the past.

54 *St. Louis of France*

Oil on canvas (octagonal), 80 by 60 cms.

St. Louis (1215-70) became King of France in 1226 as Louis IX. Involved in the Crusades, he died of plague before Tunis. Charles d'Anjou had his heart and entrails placed in the Abbey of Monreale near Palermo, while his body was buried at St.-Denis.

Possibly dating from the 1630's, No. 54 shows the melancholic refinement of many of Vignali's figures, which was to exercise considerable influence on the young Dolci, then in his studio. An octagonal *St. Michael* in a closely similar style to No. 54 is in a Florentine private collection, and both may come from a series comparable with that in the Museo degli Innocenti, Florence. An octagonal canvas showing *St. Francis of Assisi* by Carlo Dolci formerly in the Waddingham Collection, London, was particularly close in style to No. 54.

Private Collection

55 *Hagar and the Angel*

Oil on canvas, 191.6 by 131.9cms.

Signed, J.V.P. 1632

PROVENANCE: Buttery, London, 1919; Dr. Brandt; Francis Drake Brockman; Richard H. Rush

EXHIBITED: New York, Finch College Museum of Art, *The Richard H. Rush Collection*, 1971, no. 26

The theme is taken from Genesis 21: 9-21. Hagar was the Egyptian handmaiden of Sarah and mother of Abraham's first son, Ishmael. When Ishmael mocked Sarah's son Isaac, Sarah asked Abraham to banish him together with his mother. Abraham sent them into the desert of Beersheba equipped only with bread and a flask of water. When these ran out, Hagar left Ishmael beneath a bush to die (he is visible in the background of No. 55) and wept. Suddenly an angel, traditionally said to be the Archangel Michael, appeared and pointed out a nearby well from which they could drink and save themselves.

The misattribution of this characteristic Vignali to Juana Velazquez, wife of the celebrated Spanish painter on account of the initials on it, is understandable in view of the fact that many such Florentine Seicento paintings were at one time given to Spanish artists such as Murillo. Stylistically, it may be compared with *The Baptism of Christ* (Florence, Bigongiari Collection) which Mina Gregori has dated to *c.* 1635, and which also shows the same interest in verdant landscape background, rich handling of paint and delicate *sfumato* in the treatment of flesh. The theme was clearly popular with Vignali, since at least two other renderings of it are known by him. The version at Arniston House, Midlothian (repr. Ewald, op. cit.) is particularly close in format and in the relation of the angel to Hagar, while another, in the collection of the Marchesa Maria Luisa Mannucci Benincasa Capponi, Florence, is signed and dated 1630. In it, while the diaphanous drapery of the angel is similarly treated, the figure of Hagar is shown in even more contemporary dress. In every way, the picture is excellently illustrative of trends in Florentine painting in the fourth decade of the Seicento. Its deliberate evocation of facial types found especially in Andrea del Sarto, from whom the *sfumato* also derives, its naturalism coupled with an almost balletic elegance, the rendering of an Old Testament theme in modern dress, the interest in brilliant white accents deriving from Artemesia Gentileschi—all are characteristics which distinguish the school as a whole. There is a strong reflection of the type of pose which Giovanni Bilivert also favoured, and through whom gestures like that of Hagar were transmitted to the half-length females of Furini, Pignoni and Cesare Dandini.

P. & D. Colnaghi & Co.